Reader Interest

Contractors, consulting engineers, developers, local authorities

All rights reserved. No part of this publication may be reproduced or transmitted in any form or by any means, including photocopying and recording, without the written permission of the copyright holder, application for which should be addressed to the publisher. Such written permission must also be obtained before any part of this publication is stored in a retrieval system of any nature.

© CIRIA 1998

ISBN Nos:
Remedial treatment for contaminated land

Volume I	(SP101)	0 86017 396 8
Volume II	(SP102)	0 86017 397 6
Volume III	(SP103)	0 86017 398 4
Volume IV	(SP104)	0 86017 399 2
Volume V	(SP105)	0 86017 400 X
Volume VI	(SP106)	0 86017 401 8
Volume VII	(SP107)	0 86017 402 6
Volume VIII	(SP108)	0 86017 403 4
Volume IX	(SP109)	0 86017 404 2
Volume X	(SP110)	0 86017 405 0
Volume XI	(SP111)	0 86017 406 9
Volume XII	(SP112)	0 86017 407 7

Set of 12 volumes 0 86017 408 5

CLASSIFICATION	
AVAILABILITY	Unrestricted
CONTENT	Guidance based on best current practice
STATUS	Committee guided
USER	Non-specialist managers

Foreword

This volume and the other 11, which together comprise the CIRIA Report *Remedial treatment for contaminated land*, are the result of a research project carried out under contract to CIRIA by Clayton Environmental Consultants in collaboration with ECOTEC Research and Consulting Ltd and DHV Burrow-Crocker.

The report was prepared on behalf of CIRIA by:

Dr M R Harris	ECOTEC Research and Consulting Ltd (now with Clayton Environmental Consultants Ltd)
Mrs S M Herbert	TBV Science (formerly with DHV (UK) Ltd)
Mr M A Smith	Clayton Environmental Consultants Ltd

Advice on legal aspects was provided by Mrs Kathy Mylrea of Simmons and Simmons.

The project was guided and the report prepared with the help and guidance of a Project Steering Group, comprising:

Mr K J Potter (Chairman)	ICI Engineering
Dr P Bardos	Nottingham Trent University (previously at Warren Spring Laboratory)
Mr K W Brierley	British Nuclear Fuels Ltd
Dr T Cairney	W A Fairhurst & Partners
Ms J Denner	Department of the Environment
Dr H E Evans	POWERGEN
Mr R Harris	NRA Severn-Trent Region
Mr M James	Land Restoration Systems
Mr P Kirby	Trafford Park Development Corporation
Mr I Loveday	Dames and Moore International
Professor J D Mather	University of London Royal Holloway and Bedford New College
Dr S Munro	British Gas Plc
Mr S Redfearn	The BOC Foundation for the Environment
Dr J F Rees	Celtic Technologies Ltd
Mr J Thompson	Sir Owen Williams and Partners
Mr J S Watson	Scottish Enterprise
Dr P Wood	AEA Technology (previously at Warren Spring Laboratory)

CIRIA's Research Manager for the project was Dr S T Johnson.

Acknowledgements

CIRIA and the authors gratefully acknowledge the following persons and their organisations for the provision of information and comment:

Mr Y B Acar	of Louisiana State University
Mr M Beaulieu	of the Quebec Environment Ministry
Mr R Booth	of Wastewater Treatment Centre (Canada)
Mr S Bruce	of the Scottish Office
Mr J Emery	of John Emery Geotechnical Engineering
Mr M Etkind	of the Air Quality Division, DoE
Mr A Gallagher	of Department of Transport
Mr J Hansen	of Geosafe Corporation
Mr H Hatayama	of the University of California
Mr M Hinsenveld	of the University of Cincinnati
Mr R Hope	of Birmingham City Council
Mr D J Hutchison	of Environment Canada
Dr S A Jefferis	of Golder Associates
Mr R Lageman	of Geokinetics
Mr J Lapinskas	of Land Restoration Systems
Ms N Lewis	of United States Environmental Protection Agency Office of Research and Development
Mr B Neal	of the Health and Safety Executive
Mr E K Neyer	of Geraghty and Miller, Inc.
Mr J D Perry	then of Transport Research Laboratory
Mrs J Petts	of Loughborough University
Mr S Pollard	of Aspinwall and Co.
Mr H Prosser	of the Welsh Office
Mr R Ritceg	of UMATAC
Mr J Schmidt	of Wastewater Technology Center
Mr S Staps	of Grontmij NV
Mr G W Suter	of Oak Ridge National Laboratory
Mr L Traves	of Clayton Environmental Consultants Ltd
Mr J Vegter	of the Technical Soil Protection Committee (the Netherlands)
Mr M Walker	of Costain Civil Engineering Division
Mr J E H Ward	of Ministry of Environment, Lands and Parks, British Columbia
Mr P Ward	then of Warren Spring Laboratory
Mr I White	then of Edmund Nuttall Limited
Mr I L Whyte	of UMIST
Ms J Wyeth	of the Environment Unit, HSE

WA 1200191 0

ONE WEEK LOAN
Renew Books on PHONE-it: 01443 654456
Books are to be returned on or before the last date below

Glyntaff Learning Resources Centre
University of Glamorgan CF37 1DL

London, 1998

CIRIA *sharing knowledge ∎ building best practice*

6 Storey's Gate, Westminster, London SW1P 3AU
TELEPHONE 0171 222 8891   FAX 0171 222 1708
EMAIL switchboard@ciria.org.uk
WEBSITE www.ciria.org.uk

Summary

This is the first volume in CIRIA's 12-volume report about remediating contaminated land. It provides an introduction to the scope and rationale of the CIRIA research project, of which this report is the result. It also acts as a guide for users of the report, partly as a form of executive summary and partly as a consolidated and cross-referenced contents list.

Remedial treatment for contaminated land
Volume I: Introduction and guide
Construction Industry Research and Information Association
Special Publication 101, 1998

Keywords

1200 910

Air quality	XII	Local authorities	XII
Air-stripping	VIII	National policies	XII
Barriers	VI	Occupational health and safety	XII
Biological treatment	VII, VIII, IX	On and off site disposal	V
Carbon adsorption	VIII	Operational sites	X
Chemical treatments	VII, VIII, IX	Planning	XI, XII
Classification of treatment methods	IV	Post-treatment management	II
Coagulation and flocculation	VIII	Problem sites	X
Construction	X	Procurement quality management	XI
Containment	VI	Project management	XI
Contaminated land	IV	Property transaction	XII
Contaminated land policy	XII	Regulation	XII
Contaminated liquids	VIII	Regulatory bodies	XII
Contaminated material	V, X	Remedial methods	IV
Contaminated sites	II	Risk assessment	I, III
Contamination	VI	Risk management	I, III
Contract	XI	Risk-sharing	XI
Decommissioning	II	Selection of methods	IV
Decontamination	II	Sensitive-use sites	X
Demolition	II	Site assessment	III
Development control	XII	Site investigation	III
Electroremediation	VII, IX	Soil leaching	IX
Environmental assessment	XII	Soil loading	IX
Environmental protection	XII	Soil vapour extraction	IX
European policy	XII	Soil washing	VII
Excavation	V	Soil washing/flushing	IX
Ex-situ remedial methods	VII	Solvent extraction	VII
Filtration	VIII	Sorption	VIII
Groundwater	VI, VIII, IX	Stabilisation and solidification	VII, IX
Hydraulic control	VI	The re-development process	I
Infrastructure projects	X	Thermal desorption	IX
In-situ remediation	IX	Thermal treatments	VII
Isolation	VI	Vitrification	IX
Land-use policy	XII	Water quality	XII
Legislation	XII		

Contents

List of Figures vii

1 **INTRODUCTION** 1
   1.1   CIRIA programme on remediation of contaminated land...........................1
   1.2   Purpose and scope 1
   1.3   Users 3
   1.4   Relationships between volumes..4
   1.5   Professional advice 4
   1.6   Guide to the twelve volumes 4
   References...7

2 **VOLUME II DECOMMISSIONINNG, DECONTAMINATION AND
   DEMOLITION (SP102)** 8
   Contents...8
   References...10
   Index 15

3 **VOLUME III SITE INVESTIGATION AND ASSESSMENT (SP103)** 20
   Contents...20
   References...22
   Index 39

4 **VOLUME IV CLASSIFICATION AND SELECTION OF REMEDIAL
   METHODS (SP104)** 49
   Contents...49
   References...51
   Index 55

5 **VOLUME V EXCAVATION AND DISPOSAL (SP105)** 59
   Contents...59
   References...60
   Index 62

6 **VOLUME VI CONTAINMENT AND HYDRAULIC MEASURES (SP106)** 66
   Contents...66
   References...68
   Index 74

7 **VOLUME VII EX-SITU REMEDIAL METHODS FOR SOILS, SLUDGES
   AND SEDIMENTS (SP107)** 80
   Contents...80
   References...81
   Index 93

8 **VOLUME VIII IN-SITU REMEDIAL METHODS FOR CONTAMINATED
   GROUNDWATER AND OTHER LIQUIDS (SP108)** 100
   Contents...100
   References...101
   Index 104

9   **VOLUME IX IN-SITU METHODS OF REMEDIATION (SP109)** 107
     Contents 107
     References 110
     Index 121

10 **VOLUME X SPECIAL SITUATIONS (SP110)** 128
     Contents 128
     References 129
     Index 132

11 **VOLUME XI PLANNING AND MANAGEMENT (SP111)** 136
     Contents 136
     References 137
     Index 138

12 **VOLUME XII POLICY AND LEGISLATION (SP112)** 143
     Contents 143
     References 145
     Index 155

List of figures

Figure 1 *CIRIA's geo-environmental programme* 2
Figure 2 *The process of decommissioning and redeveloping a contaminated site* 6

1 Introduction

In the UK, knowledge and experience in dealing with contaminated land have been gained mainly through reclaiming contaminated derelict sites. Information on various aspects of managing contaminated land is available from a number of sources; some, particularly those concerned with treatment technologies, originate from outside the UK. This volume is one of 12 that attempt to collate this information and the underlying experience into a set of comprehensive reference and guidance documents.

1.1 CIRIA PROGRAMME ON REMEDIATION OF CONTAMINATED LAND

This report is the result of Phase I of CIRIA's contaminated land research programme, which is part of a bigger programme focusing on geo-environmental issues (Figure 1).

CIRIA's contaminated research programme comprises three phases:

Phase I

This first phase of the research programme aims to give an overview of remedial treatment for contaminated land. The work focuses on the different stages of a remedial project and issues to which clients, engineers and contractors should pay attention.

Phase II

This phase of the programme provides a state-of-the art review of two major remedial techniques for contaminated land.

Phase III

This phase of the programme consists of a series of practical demonstrations of process-based remedial techniques. The objective is to provide information and guidance to clients, engineers and contractors in the redevelopment of contaminated sites.

1.2 PURPOSE AND SCOPE

The overall objective is to assist those involved in remediating contaminated land to select and implement effective, economic and safe solutions. This volume is a guide to the other 11 and sets them in the context of UK's risk-based approved to the remediation of contaminated land.

UK practice and procedures, and international experience in the use of techniques that have seen only limited application in the UK to date, have been reviewed during the preparation of the individual volumes.

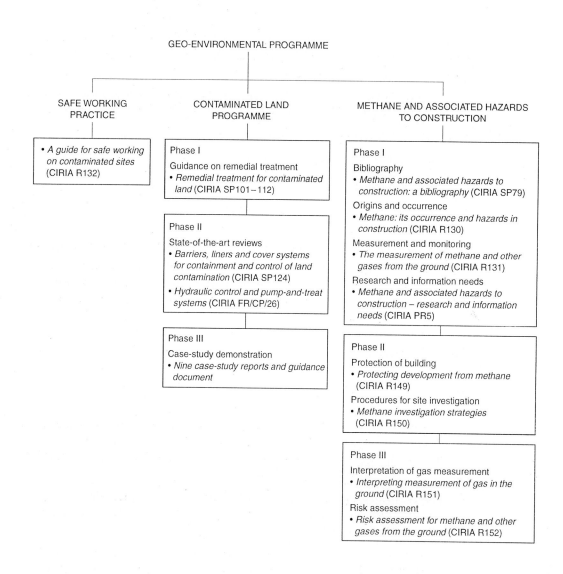

Figure 1 *CIRIA's geo-environmental programme*

These volumes:

- reflect 'good practice' not only in the context of current policy and regulations but also as they are expected to develop in the foreseeable future.

- are applicable to most contaminated land situations, including those, such as highways and operational industrial sites, which do not conform to the classic 'redevelopment' scenario.

- are designed to meet the needs of a wide range of potential users including project and development managers, consultants and contractors acting on behalf of public and private development agencies, other clients of the construction industry, central and local government, and other regulatory authorities.

Although intended to be as comprehensive as possible, in terms of addressing the full range of hazards that may be encountered, certain subjects are not specifically covered:

- the investigation of, and protection from, methane and associated gases – these are the subject of earlier CIRIA reports (CIRIA R130, R131, R149–152, SP79)

- the decontamination and remediation of radioactive contamination

- the removal and/or treatment of asbestos

- physical demolition

- grant regimes and other financial assistance.

Safety is an important and consistent theme within each volume. Individual sections refer as appropriate to the guidance available from the Health and Safety Executive, and to complementary CIRIA reports giving guidance on safe working practices on contaminated sites and on the use of substances hazardous to health in construction.

1.3   USERS

The report volumes are intended for:

- Owners of contaminated sites proposing to take remedial action as a prelude to sale or disposal of land and property; as a precursor to redevelopment; as part of a corporate environmental management programme; or because action is needed to avert a public health and/or environmental threat.

- Non-specialist managers who, faced with redeveloping or remediating contaminated sites, need information and guidance for procurement and project management purposes.

- Non-specialist civil-engineering, architectural or construction advisers providing design, supervision and inspection services in collaboration with specialist advisers.

- Contracting organisations providing groundworks, drilling, surveying, landscape, laboratory analysis, waste management services, etc. to remediation projects.

- Regulatory bodies having responsibility for public and occupational health and safety, and protection of the environment, at all stages of managing a contaminated site.

It is assumed that users will have a basic understanding of the nature of the problems of land contamination. A number of introductory texts[1,2,3] are available, which explain:

- the origins and evolution of contaminated land

- the main types of hazards which are likely to encountered on contaminated sites

- the principal potential impacts associated with the presence of contamination.

Remediation of contaminated land is a specialist activity and the management of some forms of contamination requires a high level of specialist input. For the specialist, information is provided on remedial methods that are not, so far, routinely used in the UK.

1.4   RELATIONSHIPS BETWEEN VOLUMES

The 12 volumes are intended to be used as a single source of information and guidance on the assessment and remediation of contaminated sites. Although each volume is self-contained to the extent that it covers the principal issues and procedures relevant to the subject area, reference to other volumes may be necessary for more detailed information and discussion on specific aspects. Extensive cross-referencing between the various sections and volumes is provided to help users locate this more detailed information where necessary.

Certain volumes, for example those dealing with decommissioning, site investigation, selection procedures or remedial methods, provide factual and guidance material of direct relevance to particular stages of remediation. Others, such as those concerned with policy and legislation, or planning and management issues, are broader in scope and support the technical content of the other volumes.

1.5   PROFESSIONAL ADVICE

This report is not a substitute for professional advice, which will be required in many of the situations encountered. Moreover, because of the current lack of information in some subject areas, it is difficult to provide definitive guidance on all aspects, in all cases.

Practical guidance is offered based on a comprehensive review of the current 'state of the art' and a consensus view of good practice, although several areas of uncertainty are identified, including:

- the short- and long-term impacts on human health, and the environment, associated with the presence of contaminants in soils and groundwater
- the development status of some remedial methods, and the lack of field demonstration and experience in their use
- the critical role played by case law in the interpretation of legal requirements, which means that experienced and up-to-date legal advice should always be sought, particularly on contentious issues or where uncertainties arise in connection with specific sites.

1.6   GUIDE TO THE TWELVE VOLUMES

The 12 volumes collectively address the full range of issues relevant to the remediation of contaminated land (see Table 1). Each volume is divided into sections dealing with specific aspects of the subject matter defined by the volume title. Volumes and sections are arranged in a logical order, reflecting the need for a systematic approach to the management of contaminated sites. Although each volume is self-contained, extensive cross-referencing has been provided so that users may locate more detailed information on particular topics if required. The content lists, consolidated references and indexes for the other 11 volumes are presented in Sections 2 to 12 of this volume.

The structure and content of Volumes II to XII as a whole is broadly in line with the sequence of events (from identification, through investigation and risk assessment, remediation and construction, to post-construction monitoring and maintenance) which take place on a typical contaminated site undergoing redevelopment (see Figure 2).

Figure 2 illustrates the relationships that exist between the various stages, as well as the need to apply certain technical measures (e.g. monitoring) and management procedures (planning, quality assurance/control, specification) throughout the period of development and possibly well beyond the construction phase.

Table 1 *Outline structure and contents*

Volume	Title	Outline Content
I	INTRODUCTION AND GUIDE	Aims, scope, contents list and brief summaries
II	DECOMMISSIONING, DECONTAMINATION AND DEMOLITION	Issues to be addressed and guidance on procedures
III	SITE INVESTIGATION AND ASSESSMENT	Issues to be addressed and guidance on procedures
IV	CLASSIFICATION AND SELECTION OF REMEDIAL METHODS	Classification and selection of appropriate methods and strategies
V	EXCAVATION AND DISPOSAL	Description and evaluation of methods and guidance on procedures
VI	CONTAINMENT AND HYDRAULIC MEASURES	Description and evaluation of methods and guidance on procedures
VII	EX-SITU REMEDIAL METHODS FOR SOILS, SLUDGES AND SEDIMENTS	Description and evaluation of methods and guidance on procedures
VIII	EX-SITU REMEDIAL METHODS FOR CONTAMINATED GROUNDWATER AND OTHER LIQUIDS	Description and evaluation of methods and guidance on procedures
IX	IN-SITU METHODS OF REMEDIATION	Description and evaluation of methods and guidance on procedures
X	SPECIAL SITUATIONS	Information and guidance on procedures
XI	PLANNING AND MANAGEMENT	Issues to be addressed and guidance on procedures
XII	POLICY AND LEGISLATION	Information on policy, administration and legal frameworks in UK and overseas

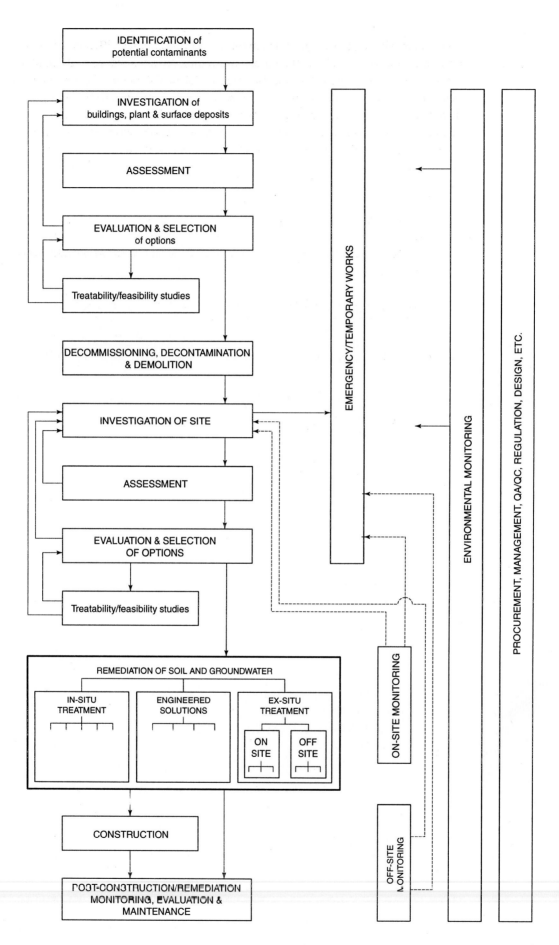

Figure 2 *The process of decommissioning and redeveloping a contaminated site*

These inter-relationships are reflected in the subject matter of the different volumes. Certain volumes (e.g. Volume II on decommissioning decontamination and demolition. Volume III on site investigation and assessment, Volume IV on selection and Volumes V–IX on different remedial methods) provide factual and guidance material that is directly relevant to particular stages of remediation. Others (e.g. Volume XI on planning and management, Volume XII on policy and legislation) are broader in scope providing conceptual or explanatory material in support of the technical content of other Volumes.

REFERENCES

1. ROYAL SOCIETY. *Risk: Analysis, perception and management.* Royal Society (London), 1991

2. LEACH B.A. and GOODGER, H.K. *Building on Derelict Land.* Special Publication 78. CIRIA (London), 1991

3. *Recycling Derelict Land.* Ed. G Fleming. Thomas Telford (London), 1991

2 Volume II Decommissioning, decontamination and demolition (SP102)

Volume II covers the period following the closure of operational facilities prior to a change in use, indefinite 'moth-balling' of existing plant and buildings or redevelopment of the site. It describes the negative public health, environmental and cost implications of poorly planned and executed site clearance operations and the need to minimise their impact on any existing soil and groundwater contamination.

The following definitions apply:

- **Decommissioning** refers to the bulk removal of hazardous materials and general housekeeping measures that will allow the site to remain safe under minimum supervision.

- **Decontamination** refers to the treatment of structures or plant contaminated during the operational life of the facility, or present as part of the fabric of the building or plant.

- **Demolition** is the controlled dismantling and removal of buildings and plant.

Volume II focuses on the first two aspects of the post-closure phase on the basis that once these are completed to a satisfactory standard, it should be possible to demolish buildings and plant along largely conventional lines.

Information is presented on preliminary and detailed site surveys and their role in deciding what decommissioning and decontamination measures are required before conventional demolition can be safely carried out. Appropriate techniques are described for process plant and surface stockpiles (e.g. drum stores) and the building fabric. Guidance is given on the implementation of post-closure measures in terms of planning and management, monitoring, health and safety and environmental protection, and post-treatment management procedures.

CONTENTS

1 **INTRODUCTION**
    1.1   Background
    1.2   Definitions
    1.3   Post-closure impacts
    1.4   Applicability of the guidance
    References

2 **THE POST-CLOSURE STRATEGY**
    2.1   Introduction
    2.2   Site surveys

2.3   Assessment of the data
2.4   Selection of methods
2.5   Post-closure operations
2.6   Legal aspects
2.7   Contractual and personnel needs
References

3   POST-CLOSURE SITE SURVEY PROCEDURES
3.1   Introduction
3.2   Desk study
3.3   Preliminary field investigation
3.4   Detailed field investigation
3.5   Health and safety considerations
References

4   ASSESSMENT OF DATA AND SELECTION OF METHODS
4.1   Introduction
4.2   Assessment of hazards and risks
4.3   Setting standards
4.4   Selection of methods
References

5   DECOMMISSIONING PROCEDURES
5.1   Introduction
5.2   Key issues
5.3   Removal of drums and other packages
5.4   Removal of surface deposits and stockpiles
5.5   Emptying plant and pipework
5.6   Emergency and temporary treatment
5.7   Health and safety during decommissioning
References

6   DECONTAMINATION PROCEDURES
6.1   Introduction
6.2   Chemical contamination
6.3   Asbestos
6.4   Explosives contamination
6.5   Biological contamination
6.6   Radiochemical contamination
6.7   Health and safety during decontamination
Reference

7   DEMOLITION PROCEDURES
7.1   Introduction
7.2   Available guidance
7.3   Impacts on residual contamination
7.4   Re-use and disposal of demolition wastes
7.5   Health and safety during demolition
References

8   PLANNING AND MANAGEMENT REQUIREMENTS
8.1   Introduction
8.2   Planning post-closure operations
8.3   Management of post-closure operations
8.4   Specification

8.5   Procurement
References

Appendix 1   Available decontamination methods
Appendix 2   Using remotely controlled equipment for hazardous decontamination
          operations
References

REFERENCES

ANON. *Damp proofing basements*. BRE Good Building Guide GBG3. Building
Research Establishment (Watford), 1991

ANON. *External rendered finishes*. BRE Digest 196. HMSO (London), 1976

ANON. *Painting walls. Part 1: Choice of paint*. BRE Digest 197. HMSO (London),
1982

ANON. *Painting walls. Part 2: Failures and remedies*. BRE Digest 198. HMSO
(London), 1982

ANON. *Replacing failed plasterwork*. BRE Good Building GBG7. Building Research
Establishment (Watford), 1991

ANON. *Rising damp in walls: diagnosis and treatment*. BRE Digest 245. HMSO
(London), 1981

ANON. *Waterproofing and repairing underground reservoir roofs*. Technical Note
145. CIRIA (London), 1991

ATKINSON, B. Industrial demolitions – A contractor's overview. In: *Proceedings of
the Second International Conference on Decommissioning Offshore, Onshore
Demolition and Nuclear Works*. Thomas Telford Ltd (London), 1990

BARKLEY, N.P. Update on building and structure decontamination. *Journal of Air &
Waste Management Association*. August 1990, 40 (8), 1174-1178

BARRY, D. Former iron and steel-making plants. In: *Contaminated Land*, Smith,
M.A. (ed.), pp 311-339. Plenum Press (New York), 1985

BAYLEY, R.G. *Chemical and hazardous materials likely to be encountered in the
closure and demolition of power stations*. Institute of Demolition Engineers
(Wentworth), 1984

BIRKHOLD, U. Decommissioning of the Niederaichback power plant. In: *Proceedings
of the Second International Conference on Decommissioning Offshore, Onshore
Demolition and Nuclear Works*. Thomas Telford Ltd (London), 1990

BRENNECKE, P. *et al*. The German approach to decommissioning of nuclear
installations. In: *Proceedings of the Third International Conference on
Decommissioning Offshore, Onshore Demolition and Nuclear Works*. Thomas Telford
Ltd (London), 1992

BRITISH STANDARDS INSTITUTION. *Code of practice for access and working scaffolds and special scaffold structures in steel.* BS 5973: 1990

BRITISH STANDARDS INSTITUTION. *Code of practice for demolition.* BS 6187: 1982

BRITISH STANDARDS INSTITUTION. *Code of practice for safe use of explosives in the construction industry.* BS 5607: 1988

CLARKE, W.H. and BOORMAN, T. Preparations for decommissioning the Windscale piles. In: *Proceedings of the Second International Conference on Decommissioning Offshore, Onshore Demolition and Nuclear Works.* Thomas Telford Ltd (London), 1990

CROWHURST, D. and MANCHESTER, S.J. *The measurement of methane and other gases from the ground.* Report 131. CIRIA (London), 1993

DELAINE, J. Hazardous materials in demolition. In: *Proceedings of the Second International Conference on Decommissioning Offshore, Onshore Demolition and Nuclear Works.* Thomas Telford Ltd (London), 1990

DOBBS, A.J. and GRANT, C. *Report on the burning of wood treated with wood preservatives containing copper, chromium and arsenic.* Building Research Establishment (Watford), 1976

DOBBS, A.J. and GRANT, C. *Report on the burning of wood treated with wood preservatives containing copper, chromium and arsenic.* Building Research Establishment (Watford), 1976

DUCKWORTH, D.V. An assessment of the environmental impact of the demolition of a lead works. *London Environmental Supplement*, No. 5. Spring 1984, 1-12

GEORGE, D.J. *Anticipated problems associated with removing asbestos coating and lagging from power stations with recommendations for future methodology.* Institute of Demolition Engineers (Wentworth), 1986

GLEN, R. *Safety aspects of disposal or demolition of industrial buildings in a toxic environment.* Institute of Demolition Engineers (Wentworth), 1991

GRANT, W.B., *et al.* Optical remote measurement of toxic gases. *Journal of Air & Waste Management Association*, January 1992, Vol. 42, (No. 1), 18-30

HEALTH AND SAFETY COMMISSION CONSTRUCTION INDUSTRY ADVISORY COMMITTEE. *Managing health and safety in construction: principles and application to main contractor/sub-contractor projects.* HMSO (London), 1987

HEALTH AND SAFETY CONSTRUCTION INDUSTRY ADVISORY COMMITTEE. *Managing health and safety in construction: management contracting.* HMSO (London), 1988

HEALTH AND SAFETY EXECUTIVE. *A guide to the Control of Industrial Major Accident Hazards Regulations 1984.* HS (R) 21 (Rev). HMSO (London), 1990

HEALTH AND SAFETY EXECUTIVE. *Asbestos: exposure limits and measurement of airborne dust concentrations.* EH 10 (Rev). HMSO (London), 1990

HEALTH AND SAFETY EXECUTIVE. *Cleaning and gas freeing of tanks containing flammable residues.* CS 15. HMSO (London), 1985

HEALTH AND SAFETY EXECUTIVE. *Control of Industrial Major Accident Hazards Regulations 1984 (CIMAH): Further guidance on emergency plan.* HS (G) 25. HMSO (London), 1985

HEALTH AND SAFETY EXECUTIVE. *Control of lead: air sampling techniques and strategies.* EH 28. HMSO (London), 1986

HEALTH AND SAFETY EXECUTIVE. *Control of lead: outside workers.* Control of lead: outside workers. EH 29. HMSO (London), 1981

HEALTH AND SAFETY EXECUTIVE. *Disposal of explosives waste and the decontamination of explosives plant.* HS (G) 36. HMSO (London), 1987

HEALTH AND SAFETY EXECUTIVE. *Electricity on construction sites.* GS 24 HMSO (London), 1983

HEALTH AND SAFETY EXECUTIVE. *Entry into confined spaces.* GS 5. HMSO (London), 1977

HEALTH AND SAFETY EXECUTIVE. *Evaluation and inspection of buildings and structures.* HS (G) 58. HMSO (London), 1980

HEALTH AND SAFETY EXECUTIVE. *Health and safety in demolition work. Part 1: preparation and planning.* GS 29/1 (Rev). HMSO (London), 1988. *Part 2: legislation.* GS 29/2. HMSO (London), 1984. *Part 3: techniques.* GS 29/3. HMSO (London), 1984. *Part 4: health hazards.* GS 29/4. HMSO (London), 1985

HEALTH AND SAFETY EXECUTIVE. *Hot work: welding and cutting on plant containing flammable materials.* HS (G) 5. HMSO (London), 1979

HEALTH AND SAFETY EXECUTIVE. *Occupational exposure limits.* EH 40/94. HMSO (London), 1994

HEALTH AND SAFETY EXECUTIVE. *Protection of workers and the general public during the development of contaminated land.* HS (G) 66. HMSO (London), 1991

HEALTH AND SAFETY EXECUTIVE. *Provision, use and maintenance of hygiene facilities for work with asbestos insulation and coatings.* EH 47 (Rev). HMSO (London), 1990

HEALTH AND SAFETY EXECUTIVE. *Removal techniques and associated waste handling for asbestos insulation, coatings and insulating board.* EH 52. HMSO (London), 1989

HEALTH AND SAFETY EXECUTIVE. *Safe use of ladders, step ladders and trestles.* GS 31. HMSO (London), 1984

HEALTH AND SAFETY EXECUTIVE. *Training of crane drivers and slingers.* GS 39. HMSO (London), 1986

HEALTH AND SAFETY EXECUTIVE. *Training operatives and supervisors for work with asbestos insulation and coatings.* EH 50. HMSO (London), 1988

HUTTON, J.C. Eleven coal-fired power stations demolished within sixteen years. In: *Proceedings of the Second International Conference on Decommissioning Offshore, Onshore Demolition and Nuclear Works.* Thomas Telford Ltd (London), 1990

JOINT ADVISORY COMMITTEE ON SAFETY AND HEALTH IN THE CONSTRUCTION INDUSTRIES. *Safety in demolition work.* HMSO (London), 1979

LEACH, B.A. and GOODGER, H.K. *Buildings on derelict land.* Special Publication 78. CIRIA (London), 1991

LEWIS, W.K. Practical aspects of redeveloping a derelict contaminated site for residential and open space use: A case study. In: *Proceedings of a Conference on Contaminated Land Policy, Regulation and Technology.* Paper No. 11. IBC (London), 1992

LOUIE, R.L. and SPEER, D.R. Decommissioning a 60-m tall exhaust stack. *Nuclear Technology* 86 (8) 120-128, 1989

MILES, J. *et al.* Ecological effects of killing Bacillus anthracies on Gruinard Island with formaldehyde. *Reclamation and Revegetation Research*, 1988, 6, 271-283

NEALE, B.S. Post-closure: Owners responsibilities. In: *Proceedings on a Conference on Decommissioning, Decontamination and Demolition: Closure of Factory Sites.* Paper No. 6. IBC (London), 1992

NICKENS, D. and MATTERN, C. Safe management of waste compressed gases. *Hazardous Materials Control.* Jan/Feb, 1991, 18-21

Radioactive Substances (Phosphatic Substances, Rare Earths etc.) Exemption Order 1962 (made under the Radioactive Substances Act, 1960)

REYNOLDS, P. Water jet danger warning. *New Civil Engineer.* 11 June 1992

ROYAL INSTITUTION OF CHARTERED SURVEYORS. *Surveying safety: A personal commitment.* RICS (London), 1991

SEILER, F. *et al.* Use of risk assessment methods in the certification of decontaminated buildings. *Risk Analysis*, 1987, 7, (4), 487-495

SMITH, M.A. Dealing with contaminated ground conditions. In: *Proceedings of the Annual Conference of the Incorporated Association of Architects and Surveyors.* Paper No. 3. IAAS (London), 1991

STEEDS, J.E., SHEPHERD, E. and BARRY, D.L. *A guide to safe working practices for contaminated sites.* Report 132. CIRIA (London), 1996

SYDDALL, J.P. Damage limitation contracting – A commercial approach to procurement of decommissioning services. In. *Proceedings of the Second International Conference on Decommissioning Offshore, Onshore Demolition and Nuclear Works.* Thomas Telford Ltd (London), 1990

TROJAK, L. The use of hydraulic attachments in demolition and decommissioning applications. In: *Proceedings of the Third International Conference on Decommissioning Offshore, Onshore Demolition and Nuclear Works.* Thomas Telford Ltd (London), 1992

UNITED STATES DEPARTMENT OF HEALTH AND HUMAN SERVICES NIOSH Worker Bulletin. *Hazardous waste sites and hazardous substance emergencies.* DHHS (NIOSH) Publications No. 83-100, 1982

UNITED STATES ENVIRONMENTAL PROTECTION AGENCY. *Assessment of technologies for the remediation of radioactivity contaminated Superfund sites.* EPA/540/2-90/001. USEPA Risk Reduction Engineering Laboratory (Washington DC), 1991

UNITED STATES ENVIRONMENTAL PROTECTION AGENCY. *Field manual for grid sampling of PCB spill sites to verify clean-up.* EPA 560/5-86-017. USEPA Office of Toxic Substances (Washington DC), 1986

UNITED STATES ENVIRONMENTAL PROTECTION AGENCY. *Guidance document for clean-up of surface tank and drum sites.* ISWER Directive 9380, 0-3. USEPA Office of Emergency and Remedial Response (Washington DC), 1987

UNITED STATES ENVIRONMENTAL PROTECTION AGENCY. *Guide for decontaminating buildings, structures, and equipment at Superfund sites.* EPA/600/2-85/028. USEPA Hazardous Waste Engineering Research Laboratory (Ohio), 1985

UNITED STATES ENVIRONMENTAL PROTECTION AGENCY. *Standard operating safety guides.* USEPA Office of Emergency and Remedial Response, Emergency Response Division, (Washington DC), 1988

UNITED STATES ENVIRONMENTAL PROTECTION AGENCY. *State-of-the-art procedures and equipment for internal inspection of underground storage tanks.* EPA/600/2-90/061. USEPA Office of Research and Development (Washington DC), 1991

UNITED STATES ENVIRONMENTAL PROTECTION AGENCY. *Technology Evaluation Report: Design and development of a pilot-scale debris decontamination system, Volume 1.* EPA/540/5-91/006a. USEPA Risk Reduction Engineering Laboratory (Ohio), 1991

WADE, R.L. and WOODYARD, J.P. *Sampling and decontamination methods for buildings contaminated with polychlorinated dibenzodioxins.* In: ACS Symposium Series No. 338, 1987, 367-375

WAGNER, K. *et al. Drum handling manual for hazardous waste sites.* Pollution Technology Review No. 143. Noyes Data Corporation (New Jersey), 1987

WHITE, S.J. *et al.* An overview of the AEA Technology decommissioning research and development programme. In: *Proceedings of the Second International Conference on Decommissioning Offshore, Onshore Demolition and Nuclear Works.* Thomas Telford Ltd (London), 1990

WHYTE, I.L. and ATKINSON, B. Demolition practice: a commentary for engineers. *Municipal Engineer*, June 1991, 91-103

WHYTE, I.L. Decommissioning of industrial sites: A review of procedures. In: *Proceedings of a Conference on Decommissioning. Decontamination and Demolition: Closure of Factory Sites.* **Paper No. 4.** IBC (London), 1992

WHYTE, I.L. Decommissioning of industrial sites: A review of procedures. In: *Proceedings of a Conference on Decommissioning, Decontamination and Demolition:* Closure of Factory Sites. Paper No. 5. IBC (London), 1992

INDEX

Note: Numbers in italics refer to Tables. B indicates a Box, and Ap indicates an Appendix

acid etching *107*
adsorption decontamination *106*Ap
air quality
   Air Quality Standards Regulations
     (1989) *20*
   legislation *20*
   protection measures 48-9
   standards for lead 41, 42B
air quality monitoring
   equipment *54*
   planning 57
   procedures 53-4
allergenic substances and sensitisers *25*
anthrax spores, decontamination 86
asbestos
   asbestos-bearing material 38
   at military site 45, 46-7
   at power stations 94
   building decontamination 80
   decontamination precautions *83*
   regulations and controls for disposal
     15
   removal/encapsulation/enclosure
     *106*Ap
assessment
   of hazard and risk 38-47
   for post-closure needs *39*
atmospheric monitoring 34B

baseline environmental monitoring, at
   military site 47
biological contamination 85-6
bleaching *107*
BS 6187 (1982) 89-90, 90B, 94
building control legislation 17
building fabric
   decontamination methods 79-80
   explosives, decontamination and
     cleaning 84B
   investigation of 32-4
   sampling methods for 34B

burning, demolition wastes 19

capacitors 29-30B
carcinogenic substances *25*
carpet sweepings, sampling 34B
case study, Strontium Semiworks
   Complex 108-10Ap
ceilings, decontamination from PCDDs
   77
Central Electricity Generating Board 94
chemicals
   locations of contaminating 78B
   requiring decontamination 78B
cinderblock walls, unpainted,
   decontamination from PCDDs *77*
Clean Air Act (1993) *20*
combustible gases, monitoring equipment
   for *54*
combustible materials *25*
compatibility testing 31, 31B
concrete floors, decontamination from
   PCDDs *77*
Construction (General Provisions)
   Regulations (1961) 17
Construction (Working Places)
   Regulations (1966) 17
containerised materials 31
contamination
   at military site 45
   biological 85-6
   contaminant migration 1, 3
   contaminated materials, during
     demolition 13
   residual, impact of 90-1
   see also decontamination
contingency plans 68
contractors
   payment of 100-1
   relationships with 99-100
   specialised 101
Control of Pollution Act (COPA) (1974)

20
Amendment (1989) *21*
Control of Pollution (Special Wastes)
Regulations (1980) 20
Control of Substances Hazardous to
Health (COSHH) (1988) 17, 40
Controlled Waste (Registration of
Carriers and Seizure of Vehicles)
Regulations (1992) *21*
Controlled Waste Regulations (1992) *21*
coring, for sampling 34B
corrosive substances *25*

data assessment 38-47
conduct of 12
objectives 11
post-closure plan 12
decommissioning
definition 2
emergency/temporary treatment 69-72
health and safety during 72
method selection 13, 43-5, *44*
methods for 42-7
planning the operation 56-7
planning permission for 16
plant and pipework emptying 64-8
post-closure operations for 14
post-treatment management 63-4
procedures 48-72
on sites with uncertainty 9
specifications for 98
decontamination
acid etching *107*
adsorption *106*
asbestos precautions *83*
bleaching *107*
chemical 77-82
chemical plant example *75*
chemicals, materials and their location
78B
definition 2
drilling and spalling *107*
dusting/vacuuming/wiping *106*
encapsulation/enclosure *106*
equipment for 81
explosives 83, 84B
flaming *107*
gritblasting *106*
health and safety during 86
hydroblasting/water washing *106*
method applicability/performance *106-
7*
method selection 13, 43-5, *44*, 86
methods available 77B, *104*Ap, *105*Ap
microbial degradation *107*Ap

paint removal/coating *106*Ap
photochemical degradation *107*Ap
planning permission for 16
plant, procedures for 78-9
polychlorinated dibenzodioxins
(PCDDs) *77*
post-closure operations for 14-15
post-treatment management 82
and previous refurbishment 76
procedures 75-86
radiochemical 86
scarification *106*Ap
sealing methods 80-1
solvent washing *107*Ap
steam cleaning *107*Ap
Strontium Semiworks Complex 108Ap
techniques for plant structures and
building fabric 43B
vapour-phase solvent extraction *107*Ap
and vermin 76
waste disposal 81-2
demolition
code of practice for, BS 6187 (1982)
89-90, 90B
common techniques 43B
definition 2
health and safety during 93
method selection 13-14
military site 46
post-closure operations for 15
procedures 89-93
residual contamination 90-2
residues 3
on sites with uncertainty 9
uncontrolled *4*
waste burning 19
waste re-use and disposal 92
demolition contracts, payment by
recovered materials 3
Department of the Environment Circular
(8/87) 16
desk studies 10
and health and safety 35
for post-closure site surveys 22-3
drainage, for environmental protection 49
drainage systems *26*
drilled samples 34B
drilling and spalling *107*Ap
drummed materials 31, *32*
drums
abandoned *52*
characteristics 51
removal of 50-8
removal operations 53
transfer preparations 53

dry linings for sealing 80
dry wipe sampling techniques *33*
dusting 79, *106*Ap
Duty of Care
   and demolition wastes 92
   and Environmental protection Act
     (EPA) (1990) 15, 19
Duty of Care Regulations (1991) *21*

EC Directives on Temporary or Mobile
   Sites 17
effluent treatment systems *26*
electrical equipment, decontamination
   from PCDDs 77B
electricity sub station, transformers and
   capacitors 29-30B
emergency measures, short term *27*
emergency provision/response 49, 68
emergency treatment
   decommissioning 69-72
   monitoring 70-1
   planning 70-1
   post-treatment management 71-2
   problem situations 70B
   temporary measures 70B
encapsulation/enclosure *106*Ap
environmental protection
   during decommissioning 67
   during post-closure 18-19, 41, 48-9
   planning for 57
Environmental protection Act (EPA)
   (1990) *20*, 67
   and Duty of Care 15
   Duty of Care on waste disposers 19
   and public health 18
environmental protection legislation 18-
   19, *20-1*
explosives
   building decontamination 84B
   decontamination control 84B
   plant cleaning, dismantling and
     decontamination 84B

fabric, sampling 34B
field investigations
   elements of plan 29B
   for post-closure site surveys 28-34
flaming *107*Ap
flue dusts, disposal 61
fungi, contamination by *85*

galvanised painted ceilings and walls,
   decontamination from PCDDs *77*
gases, toxic, narcotic, flammable or
   explosive *25*

General Development Orders 16
gritblasting *106*Ap
ground and water protection 49

hazardous materials
   during demolition 13
   examples of industries with 1B
   examples of *25*
   physically *25*
   as residues 1
hazards, assessment of 38-47
health and safety
   and decommissioning procedures 50
   during decommissioning 72
   during decontamination 86
   during demolition 93
   and post-closure surveys 35
Health and Safety at Work Act (HSWA)
   (1974) 17, 18
Health and Safety Executive (HSE) 16,
   45
Health and Safety Guidance Note GS29
   94
health and safety legislation 17-18
hexavalent chrome stockpiled 59B
hydroblasting/water washing *106*Ap

industrial vacuum loaders 56
industrial wastes *see* wastes
industries with hazardous substances 1B
injection for sealing 80
insect contamination *85*

laboratory facilities *26*
landowner/operator responsibilities 1, 21
lead-in-air standard 41, 42B
levelling operations 3
liquids
   bulking and consolidation protocol *57*
   flammable *25*
   in porous materials 80
local community interest/hostility 50
loose dust, sampling 34B
lump sum contracts 100

maintenance depots *26*
Management of Health and Safety at
   Work Regulations (1992) 17
material segregation/characterisation 54-
   5
   broad waste categories 55B
materials
   problem 60-1
   see also wastes
Maximum Exposure Limits (MELs) 40

microbial degradation *107*Ap
migration of contaminants 1, 3
military site, post-closure case study 45-7
monitoring
   for decommissioning 49
   emergency treatment 70-1
   toxic gases/vapours *54*
munitions, disposal 60
mutagenic substances *25*

National Rivers Authority 16

occupants of buildings, health and safety
   of 40-1
Occupational Exposure Standards (OESs)
   40
occupational health and safety 17-18, 40
Occupiers Liability Acts (1957 and 1984)
   18
operator/landowner responsibilities 1, 21
oxygen deficiency, monitoring equipment
   for *54*

paint removal/coating *106*Ap
pathogenic agents *25*
pathogens, contamination by 85, *85*
PCB (polychlorinated biphenyl) 29-30B,
   94
   on contaminated sites 33
PCDDs (polychlorinated dibenzodioxins)
   77
photochemical degradation *107*Ap
phytotoxic metals *25*
pipework emptying 64-8
   leaving safe 67-8
   likely materials for 66, 66B
   planning 66-8
   spillage/contamination from *64, 65*
planning, for environmental protection
   49-50
planning permission, for decontamination
   and decommissioning 16
plant
   decontamination procedures for 78-9
   emptying of liquids *see* pipework
      emptying
   explosives, cleaning and
      decontamination 84B
polychlorinated biphenyl *see* PCB
polychlorinated dibenzodioxins (PCDDs)
   77
porous materials, contaminated 80
porous/permeable building materials 78B
post-closure
   contractual and personnel needs 19-21

desk studies for 22-4
and environmental protection 18-19,
   41
impacts 3
legal aspects 15-19
management of 97-8
operations 14-15
periods 9
planning operations 95-7, *96*
plans for 6, 12
post-treatment management 98
preliminary field investigations 24-8
procurement 99-101
and public health 18, 41
site survey procedures 22-36
site surveys for field investigations 28-
   34
technical specifications for 98-9
post-closure strategy 6-21
   flow charts for *7, 8, 9*
   phased approach 9
post-treatment management 50, 90
power generation equipment *26*
preliminary field investigations, for post-
   closure 24-8
processing areas *26*
public health, and post-closure 18, 41

radiation, monitoring equipment for *54*
radioactive materials/substances *25*
   disposal 61
Radioactive Substances Act (1993) *21*
radiochemical decontamination 86
reactive inorganic salts *25*
recirculating wash systems 79
Regulations (Construction (Design and
   Management) Regulations 1994) 17
residual contamination 90-1
   access and space restraints 91
   emissions with demolition 91-2, *91*
   working methods 91
residual materials 31-2
   hazardous 1
risk
   assessment 38-9, 40
   evaluation 11
   standard setting 39-42
rubble, disposal 61

safe working practices 55
safety
   during decommissioning 68
   see also health and safety
safety teams 35
scarification *106*

sealing methods 80-1
  above/below ground options *81*
  internal/external options *81*
security of sites 2, 6
self-ignition materials *25*
site closure 9
site surveys, objectives and phasing 10, *11*
skin damaging substances *25*
slags, disposal 60
solids, flammable *25*
solvent cleaning 79
solvent washing *107*Ap
South of Scotland Electricity Board 94
special wastes 19
specialist expertise 101
specifications for post-closure 98-9, *98*
steam cleaning 79, *107*
steel walls, decontamination from PCDDs *77*
stockpiles *see* surface deposits
storage areas *26*
stratified random sampling 31
Strontium Semiworks Complex, case study 108-10Ap
surface abrasion/chippings, sampling methods 34B
surface deposits
  recovery for re-use 60
  removal 58-64
  typical materials 59B
surface wipe samples 34B

tank purging 90
temporary treatment *see* emergency treatment
tender documents 21
teratogenic substances *25*
timber, treated, disposal of 60
toxic gases/vapours, monitoring
  equipment for *54*
transformers 29-30B
treatment/recovery/disposal route planning 67
tree felling, at military site 46

unloading areas 48

vacuuming 79, *106*Ap
vapour-phase solvent extraction *107*Ap
vehicles 48, 67
  routes and planning conditions 50
ventilation and gas filtration/conditioning systems *26*
vermin *25*, *85*
  and decontamination 76

waste disposal areas *26*
waste management 20-1
Waste Management Licensing Regulations (1994) *21*
Waste Regulation Authorities 12
wastes
  collection and disposal 81-2
  and health and safety 18
  legal disposal of 19
  segregation of *56*
  special wastes 19
Water Industry Act (1991) *20*
water protection 49
water quality *20*
Water Resources Act (1991) *20*
water washing/hydroblasting 79, *106*Ap
wet and dry wipe sampling techniques *33*
wheel washing 49
wiping 79, *106*Ap
workshops *26*

zootoxic metals *25*

3   Volume III Site investigation and assessment (SP103)

Volume III covers the critical role played by site investigation in managing the risks associated with contaminated land. It emphasises the need for a phased approach to investigation for the purposes of gathering the information needed for risk assessment and, where appropriate, the selection, design and implementation (including post-treatment validation) of remedial works.

Volume III also stresses the need to address contamination, geological and hydrological aspects on an integrated basis so that hazard-pathway-target scenarios can be fully characterised and evaluated.

Information and guidance is presented on:

- planning investigation work so that is generates sufficient good quality data to effectively manage risks

- the implementation of site investigation work so that it is safe, effective and economic

- sampling and analysis requirements to ensure that all the data obtained are reliable and fully representative of site conditions.

Formal risk assessment procedures are introduced and their relationship with site investigation activities discussed. The role of published guidelines (e.g. the UK Interdepartmental Committee on the Redevelopment of Contaminated Land trigger concentration values) and standards in assessing the significance of observed levels of contamination, and in identifying site-specific remedial objectives, is discussed.

CONTENTS

1 INTRODUCTION
    1.1   A Risk management approach
    1.2   The purpose of investigation
    1.3   Types of investigation
    References

2 PLANNING THE INVESTIGATION
    2.1   Scope
    2.2   Setting objectives
    2.3   Phasing of the investigation
    2.4   Preliminary investigation
    2.5   Exploratory investigation
    2.6   Detailed investigation
    2.7   Integration of investigation procedures

2.8   Reporting
2.9   Ecological assessment
2.10   Post-closure survey
References

3   **IMPLEMENTATION OF SITE INVESTIGATIONS**
3.1   Project management
3.2   Legal aspects
3.3   Procurement
3.4   Specification
3.5   Selection of appropriate specialists
3.6   Quality management
3.7   Health and safety
3.8   Environmental protection requirements
3.9   Long-term sampling and off site works
References

4   **SAMPLING AND TESTING**
4.1   Developing a strategy
4.2   Sampling strategies
4.3   Sampling of soils and similar materials
4.4   Sampling groundwater
4.5   Sampling surface water
4.6   Analytical and testing strategies
References

5   **RISK ASSESSMENT**
5.1   Introduction
5.2   Objectives and scope
5.3   Concepts and definitions
5.4   Information requirements
5.5   Conducting a site-specific risk assessment
5.6   Use of models in risk assessment
5.7   Uses of risk assessment
5.8   Communication of risks
References

6   **GUIDELINES AND STANDARDS**
6.1   Scope
6.2   Types of guidelines and standards
6.3   The use of guidelines and standards for assessment
6.4   The use of guidelines and standards for remediation
6.5   Dealing with variability
6.6   UK guidelines and standards
References

7   **INVESTIGATION FOR COMPLIANCE AND PERFORMANCE**
7.1   Scope
7.2   Excavation
7.3   Performance of ex-situ process-based methods
7.4   Remediation of groundwater through ex-situ treatment (pump and treat)
7.5   Performance of in-situ processes
7.6   Monitoring containment methods
7.7   Evaluation of remedial methods
References

Appendix 1   Guidance documents on site investigation
Appendix 2   Information sources for desk study
Appendix 3   Possible hypotheses on the distribution of contaminants
Appendix 4   Guidance on specialists
Appendix 5   Key elements in the NAMAS accreditation scheme
Appendix 6   Investigation techniques
Appendix 7   Analytical and testing strategies and methods
Appendix 8   Important concepts and terms for risk assessment
Appendix 9   Quantifying human health risks
Appendix 10   Examples of modelling in risk assessment
Appendix 11   International guidelines and standards
Appendix 12   Ecological risk assessment [1]

REFERENCES

ADAMS, W.J., KIMERLE, R.A. and BARNETT, J.W. Sediment quality and aquatic life assessment. *Environmental Science and Technology*, 1992, **26**(10), 1864-1875

ALLOWAY, B.J. *Heavy Metals in Soils.* B. Alloway (ed.). Blackie (Glasgow), 1990

AMERICAN CHEMICAL SOCIETY. *Proceedings of the Eighth Annual Waste Testing and Quality Assurance Symposium.* ACS (Arlington, VA), 1992

AMERICAN SOCIETY FOR TESTING AND MATERIALS. *Annual Book of ASTM Standards, Section 11: Water and environmental technology.* ASTM (Philadelphia), annual publication

AMERICAN SOCIETY FOR TESTING AND MATERIALS. *Standard test method for potential expansion of aggregates from hydration reactions.* ASTM D4792. ASTM (Philadelphia), reviewed annually

AMERICAN SOCIETY FOR TESTING AND MATERIALS. *Standard practice for the design and installation of groundwater monitoring wells in aquifers.* ASTM D5092. ASTM (Philadelphia), 1990 [revised annually]

ANON. Advanced soil gas sampling maps hydrocarbon in contaminated land. *Industrial Waste Management*, 1994 (May) pp 186-70

ANON. *Building Regulation 1991: Approved Document C: Site Preparation and Resistance to Moisture.* HMSO (London), 1992

ANON. *Client's guide to quality assurance in construction.* Special Publication 55. CIRIA (London), 1988

ANON. *National quality assurance forum for construction.* Special Publication 61. CIRIA (London), 1988

ANON. Risk assessment methods for deriving clean-up levels. *The Hazardous Waste Consultant*, May/June 1991, 1.1-1.6

ASSOCIATION OF ENVIRONMENTAL CONSULTANCIES. *Code of Practice (Contaminated Land).* AEC, 1994

ASSOCIATION OF GEOTECHNICAL SPECIALISTS. *Quality management in geotechnical engineering, a practical approach.* AGS, 1990

ASSOCIATION OF GROUND INVESTIGATION SPECIALISTS. Specification for Ground Investigations. *Ground Engineering,* **12** (5), 1979

AUSTRALIAN AND NEW ZEALAND ENVIRONMENT AND CONSERVATION COUNCIL/NATIONAL HEALTH AND MEDICAL RESEARCH COUNCIL. *Australian and New Zealand guidelines for the assessment and management of contaminated sites.* ANZECC/NHMRC, 1992

BARBER, J.N. *Quality management in construction: contractual aspects.* Special Publication 84. CIRIA (London), 1992

BARRY, D.L. Former iron and steelmaking plants. In: *Contaminated Land: Reclamation and Treatment.* Smith, M.A. (ed.) Plenum (London) 1985, pp 311-340

BAYNE, C.K., SCHMOYER, D.D. and JENKINS, R.A. Practical reporting times for environmental samples. *Environmental Science and Technology,* 1994, **28** (8), 1430-1436

BRIDGES, E.M. *The use of remote sensing in the identification, mapping and monitoring of contaminated land.* University of Swansea (Swansea), 1984

BRITISH DRILLING ASSOCIATION LTD. *Ground investigation drillers' accreditation scheme.* BDA (Brentwood)

BRITISH DRILLING ASSOCIATION. *Code of safe drilling practice, Part 1: surface drilling.* BDA (Brentwood), 1981

BRITISH DRILLING ASSOCIATION. *Guidelines for the drilling of landfill, contaminated land and adjacent areas.* BDA (Brentwood), 1991

BRITISH STANDARDS INSTITUTION. BS 1047: *Specification for air-cooled blastfurnace slag aggregate for use in construction.* BSI (London), 1983

BRITISH STANDARDS INSTITUTION. *Code of Practice for Ground Investigation.* BS 5930:1981. BSI (London), 1981

BRITISH STANDARDS INSTITUTION. *Code of Practice for Site Investigations.* BS 5930:1981. BSI (London), 1981

BRITISH STANDARDS INSTITUTION. *Code of Practice for the Identification of Contaminated Land and for its Investigation.* DD175:1988 Draft for Development. BSI (London), 1988

BRITISH STANDARDS INSTITUTION. *Quality Systems.* BS EN ISO 9000: 1994. BSI (London), 1994

BRITISH STANDARDS INSTITUTION. *Quality Vocabulary.* BS 4778. BSI (London), 1987 and 1991

BRITISH STANDARDS INSTITUTION. *Water Quality: Part 6: Sampling: Section 6.1 Guidance on the design of sampling programmes.* BS 6068: Part 6: Section 6.1: 1981 (confirmed 1990) [ISO 5667/1 – 1980]. BSI (London), 1991

BRITISH STANDARDS INSTITUTION. *Water Quality: Part 6: Sampling: Section 6.2 Guidance on sampling techniques.* BS 6068: Part 6: Section 6.2: 1991 [ISO 5667/2 – 1991]. BSI (London), 1991

BRITISH STANDARDS INSTITUTION. *Water Quality: Part 6: Sampling: Section 6.3 Guidance on the preservation and handling of samples.* BS 6068: Part 6: Section 6.3: 1986 [ISO 5667/3 – 1985]. BSI (London), 1986

BRITISH STANDARDS INSTITUTION. *Water Quality: Part 6: Sampling: Section 6.4 Guidance on sampling from lakes, natural and man made.* BS 6068: Part 6: Section 6.4: 1987 [ISO 5667/4 – 1987]. BSI (London), 1987

BRITISH STANDARDS INSTITUTION. *Water Quality: Part 6: Sampling: Section 6.6 Guidance on sampling of rivers and streams of samples.* BS 6068: Part 6: Section 6.6: 1991 [ISO 5667/6 – 1991]. BSI (London), 1991

BRITISH STANDARDS INSTITUTION. *Water Quality: Part 6: Sampling: Section 6.11 Guidance on sampling of groundwaters.* BS 6068: Part 6: Section 6.11: 1993 [ISO 5667/11 – 1993]. BSI (London), 1993

BRITISH STANDARDS INSTITUTION. *Water Quality: Part 6: Sampling: Section 6.12 Guidance on sampling of sediments.* BS 6068: Part 6: Section 6.12: 1993 [ISO 5667/12 – 1993]. BSI (London), 1993

BRITISH STANDARDS INSTITUTION/INTERNATIONAL ORGANISATION FOR STANDARDISATION. ISO DIS 10381-6: *Soil Quality – Sampling: Part 6: Guidance on the collection, handling and storage of soil for aerobic microbial processes in the laboratory.* Available from BSI (London), 1993

BUILDING RESEARCH ESTABLISHMENT. *Construction of new buildings on gas contaminated ground.* BRE (Garston), 1991

BUILDING RESEARCH ESTABLISHMENT. *Radon: Guidance on protective measures for new dwellings.* BRE (Garston), 1991

BUILDING RESEARCH ESTABLISHMENT. *Sulphate and acid resistance of concrete in the ground.* BRE Digest 363. BRE (Garston), 1991

BURTON, G.A. and SCOTT, K.J. Sediment toxicity evaluations: their niche in ecological assessments. *Environmental Science and Technology,* 1992, **26** (11), 2068-2075

CAIRNEY, T. (ed.) *Contaminated Land: Problems and Solutions.* Blackie Academic and Professional (Glasgow), 1993

CAIRNEY, T. Long-term monitoring of reclaimed sites. In: *Reclaiming Contaminated Land.* Cairney, T. (ed.) Blackie (Glasgow), 1987, pp 170-180

CAIRNEY, T. and SHARROCK, T. Clean cover technology. In: *Contaminated Land: Problems and Solutions,* Cairney, T. (ed.) Blackie (London), 1993, pp 84-110

CALABRESE, E. J. and KOSTECKI, P. T. *Soils contaminated by petroleum: environmental and health effects.* Wiley (Chichester), 1988

CANADIAN COUNCIL OF ENVIRONMENT MINISTERS. *A protocol for the derivation of ecological effects-based and human health based quality criteria for contaminated sites.* CCME (Winnipeg), 1993

CANADIAN COUNCIL OF ENVIRONMENT MINISTERS. *Interim CCME environmental quality criteria for contaminated sites.* CCME EPC-CS34. CCEM (Winnipeg), 1991

CANADIAN COUNCIL OF ENVIRONMENT MINISTERS. *Proposed protocols for derivation of water quality guidelines for the protection of agricultural water uses.* Water Quality Branch, Environment Canada (Ottawa), 1991

CANADIAN COUNCIL OF MINISTERS OF THE ENVIRONMENT. *Guidance Manual on sampling, analysis and data management for contaminated sites, Volume 1: Main Report.* CCME NCS 62E. CCME (Winnipeg), 1993

CANADIAN COUNCIL OF MINISTERS OF THE ENVIRONMENT. *Guidance Manual on sampling, analysis and data management for contaminated sites, Volume 2: Analytical method summaries.* CCME NCS 66E. CCME (Winnipeg) 1993

CANADIAN COUNCIL OF MINISTERS OF THE ENVIRONMENT. *National classification system for contaminated sites* (final draft). CCME (Winnipeg), 1991

CANADIAN COUNCIL OF RESOURCE AND ENVIRONMENT MINISTERS. *Canadian Water Quality Guidelines.* CCREM (Winnipeg), 1987

CARDWELL, R.D., PARKHURST, B.R., WARREN-HICKS, W. and VOLOSIN, J.S. Aquatic ecological risk. *Water Environment and Technology,* 1993, 5(4), 47-51

CHEESEMAN, R.V. and WILSON, A.L. (revised by GARDNER, M.J.). *A manual for analytical control for the water industry.* Water Research Centre (Medmenham), 1989

CLARK, L. *The field guide to water wells and boreholes.* Geological Society (London), 1988

CRIPPS, J.C., BELL, F.G. and CULSHAW, M.G. (eds). *Groundwater in engineering geology.* Geological Society (London), 1986

CROWHURST, D., and MANCHESTER S.J. *The measurement of methane and other gases from the ground.* Report 131. CIRIA (London), 1993

DARRACOTT, B.W. and McCANN, D.M. Planning engineering geophysical surveys. In: *Geological Society Special Publication No. 2.* Geological Society (London), 1986, pp 85-90

DAVIES, B.E. (ed.) *Applied soil trace elements.* Wiley (London), 1980

DENNEMAN, C.A.C. and ROBBERSE, J.G. Ecotoxicological risk assessment as a base for development of soil quality criteria. In: *Proceedings of the Third International KfK/TNO Conference on Contaminated Soil.* Kluwer (Dordrecht), 1990, pp 157-164

DENNER, J. Contaminated land: a framework for risk assessment. In: *Proceedings Conference Contaminated Land: Developing a Risk Management Strategy.* IBC (London), 1994

DEPARTMENT OF THE ENVIRONMENT (TOXIC SUBSTANCES DIVISION). *Environmental hazard assessment: benzene.* Building Research Establishment (Garston), 1991 [other titles include: toluene, di-(2-ethylhexyl) phthalate and 1,1,1 trichloroethane]

DEPARTMENT OF THE ENVIRONMENT. *EC Directive on protection of groundwater against pollution by certain dangerous substances (80/68/EEC): Classification of listed substances.* Circular 20/90. DOE (London), 1990

DEPARTMENT OF THE ENVIRONMENT. *Guidance on the Assessment and Redevelopment of Contaminated Land.* ICRCL Guidance Note 59/83 (2nd edition). DOE (London), 1987

DEPARTMENT OF THE ENVIRONMENT. ICRCL Industry Profiles. DOE (London)

DEPARTMENT OF THE ENVIRONMENT. *Inputs of Dangerous Substances to Water: Proposals for a Unified System of Control.* DOE (London), 1988

DEPARTMENT OF THE ENVIRONMENT. *Landfilling Wastes.* Waste Management Paper No 26. HMSO (London), 1986

DEPARTMENT OF THE ENVIRONMENT. *Landfill Gas.* Waste Management Paper No. 27 (2nd edition). HMSO (London), 1991

DEPARTMENT OF THE ENVIRONMENT. *Notes on the fire hazards of contaminated land.* ICRCL Guidance Note 61/84 (2nd edition). DOE (London), 1986

DEPARTMENT OF THE ENVIRONMENT. *Notes on the Restoration and Aftercare of Metalliferous Mining Sites for Pasture and Grazing.* ICRCL Guidance Note 70/90. DOE (London), 1990

DEPARTMENT OF THE ENVIRONMENT. *Problems arising from the redevelopment of gas works and similar sites.* DOE (London), 1987

DEPARTMENT OF THE ENVIRONMENT. *Risk assessment and characterisation procedures for sites which may be contaminated.* DOE (London)

DEPARTMENT OF THE ENVIRONMENT. *River Quality: the Government's Proposals.* Consultation paper. DOE (London), 1992

DEPARTMENT OF THE ENVIRONMENT. *The Government's Response to the First Report from the House of Commons Select Committee on the Environment: Contaminated Land.* Cm 1161. HMSO (London), 1990

DEPARTMENT OF THE ENVIRONMENT. *Water and the Environment: the implementation of the European Community Directives on pollution caused by certain dangerous substances discharges into the aquatic environment.* Circular 7/89. DOE (London), 1989

DEPARTMENT OF THE ENVIRONMENT/WELSH OFFICE/SCOTTISH OFFICE. *Landfill completion.* Waste Management Paper No. 26A. HMSO (London), 1993

Directive concerning the methods of measurement and frequency of sampling and analysis of surface water intended for the abstraction of drinking water in Member States. Directive 79/869/EEC. OJ L271, October 1979

Directive on pollution caused by certain substances discharged into the aquatic environment of the Community. Directive 76/464/EEC. OJ L129, May 1976

Directive on the quality of fresh waters needing protection or improvement in order to support fish life. Directive 78/659/EEC. OJ L222, August 1978

DURDA, J.L. Ecological risk assessments under Superfund. *Water Environment and Technology,* 1993, **5**(4), 42-46

EDULJEE, G. Application of risk assessment to contaminated land. In: *Proceedings of a Conference on Contaminated Land Policy, Economics and Technology.* Paper No.2. IBC (London), 1993

EMERY, J.J. A simple test procedure for evaluating the potential expansion of steel slag. In: *Proc. 1975 Annual Conference of the Roads and Transportation Association of Canada, Toronto 1975*

ENDS. *Dangerous Substances in Water: A Practical Approach.* Environmental Data Services (London), 1992

ENDS. *Directory of Environmental Consultants.* Third edition (1992/93). Environmental Data Services (London), 1992

ENGINEERING COUNCIL. *Guidelines on risk issues.* Engineering Council (London), 1993

FERGUSON, C. A statistical basis for spatial sampling of contaminated land. *Ground Engineering,* 1992, (June), 34-38

FERGUSON, C. *Sampling strategies for contaminated land.* CLR Report No. 4. Department of the Environment (London), 1994

FERGUSON, C. and DENNER, J. Soil remediation guidelines in the United Kingdom: A new risk based approach. In: *Proceedings of a Conference on Developing Clean-up Standards for Contaminated Soil, Sediment and Groundwater: How Clean is Clean?.* Water and Environment Federation (Alexandria VA), 1993, pp 205-212

Final Report NATO Committee on the Challenges of Modern Society Pilot Study: Demonstration of Remedial Action Technologies for Contaminated Land and Groundwater, Volume 1. EPA/600/R 93/012a. USEPA Risk Reduction Engineering Laboratory (Cincinnati), 1993

FLEMING, G. (ed.). *Recycling Derelict Land.* Thomas Telford Ltd (London), 1991

FOLKESTAD, B. Approach to clean up standards in Norway. In: *Proceedings of a Conference on Developing Clean-up Standards for Contaminated Soil, Sediment and Groundwater: How Clean is Clean?.* Water and Environment Federation (Alexandria VA), 1993, pp 187-194

FREEZE, R.A. and CHERRY, J.A. *Groundwater.* Prentice Hall (Englewood Cliffs NJ), 1979

GUERRIERIO, M.M. In-situ vacuum extraction Verona Well Field Superfund Site, Battle Creek, Michigan. *Final Report NATO Committee on the Challenges of Modern*

Society Pilot Study: Demonstration of Remedial Action Technologies for Contaminated Land and Groundwater, Volume 1. EPA/600/R-93/012a. USEPA Risk Reduction Engineering Laboratory (Cincinnati), 1993, pp 1032 -1052

Guidelines for exposure assessment. *Notice Federal Register*, Vol 57, No 104 (29 May 1992), pp 22888-22938

HAMILTON, E.I. Analysis for Trace Elements I: Sample treatment and laboratory quality control. In: *Applied Science Trace Elements*, B.E. Davies (ed.). Wiley (Chichester), 1980, pp 21-68

HAMILTON, E.I. Analysis for Trace Elements II: Instrumental analysis. In: *Applied Science Trace Elements*, B.E. Davies (ed.). Wiley (Chichester), 1980, pp 69-130

HARRIS, R. and THOMAS, C.A. Contaminated land and water quality standards. In: *Proc. Conference on Contaminated Land: Policy, Risk Management and Technology, London 1994*. IBC Technical Services (London), 1994

HEALTH AND SAFETY EXECUTIVE. *COSHH and Peripatetic Workers.* HS (G)77. HMSO (London), 1992

HEALTH AND SAFETY EXECUTIVE. *Disposal of explosives waste and the decontamination of explosives plant.* HS (G) 36. HMSO (London), 1987

HEALTH AND SAFETY EXECUTIVE. *Occupational Exposure Limits 1994.* EH 40/94. HMSO (London), 1994

HEALTH AND SAFETY EXECUTIVE. *Evaluation and Inspection of Structures.* HS (G)58. HMSO (London), 1990

HEALTH AND SAFETY EXECUTIVE. *Protection of workers and the general public during the development of contaminated land.* HS (G) 66. HMSO (London), 1991

HEALTH AND SAFETY EXECUTIVE. *Risk criteria for land-use planning in the vicinity of major industrial hazards.* HMSO (London), 1989

HEALTH AND SAFETY EXECUTIVE. *The tolerability of risk from nuclear power stations.* HMSO (London), 1988

HEALTH AND WELFARE CANADA. *Guidelines for Canadian Drinking Water Quality.* 4th edition. Canadian Government Publishing Centre (Ottawa), 1989

HER MAJESTY'S INSPECTORATE OF POLLUTION. *Chief Inspector's Guidance to Inspectors, Environmental Protection Act, 1990.* Process Guidance Notes (various titles). HMSO (London)

HEWITT, C.N. *Methods of Environmental Data Analysis,* C.N. Hewitt (ed.). Elsevier (London), 1992

HINSENVELD, M. A sound and practical method to determine the quality of stabilization. In: *Proceedings of the First International NATO/CCMS Conference on the Evaluation of Demonstrated and Emerging Technologies for the Treatment and Cleanup of Contaminated Land and Groundwater (Phase II), (Budapest).* USEPA Risk Reduction Engineering Laboratory (Cincinnati), 1992

HINSENVELD, M. *Leaching and volatilization from cement stabilized wastes.* Kluwer (Dordrecht), 1993

HOBSON, D.M. Rational site investigation. In: *Contaminated Land: Problems and Solutions,* T. Cairney (ed.) Blackie Academic (London), 1993, pp 29-67

HOFMAN, E.L. *et al.* Setting goals for contaminated sites: towards a nationally consistent approach in Canada. In: *Proceedings of a Conference on Developing Clean-up Standards for Contaminated Soil, Sediment and Groundwater: How Clean is Clean?.* Water and Environment Federation (Alexandria VA), 1993, pp 69-91

HOOKER, P.J. and BANNON, M.P. *Methane: Its occurrence and hazards in construction.* Report 130. CIRIA (London), 1993

HUGGETT, R.J., UNGER, M.A., SELIGMAN, P.F. and VALKIRS, A.O. The marine biocide tributyltin: assessing and managing the environmental risks. *Environmental Science and Technology,* 1992, **26**(2), 232-237.

INSTITUTION OF CHEMICAL ENGINEERS. *Nomenclature for hazard and risk assessment in the process industries.* IChemE (Rugby), 1985

INSTITUTION OF CIVIL ENGINEERS. *ICE Conditions of Contract for Ground Investigation.* Thomas Telford (London), 1983

INSTITUTION OF CIVIL ENGINEERS. *Inadequate site investigation.* Thomas Telford (London), 1991

INSTITUTION OF CIVIL ENGINEERS. *Specification for ground investigation.* Thomas Telford (London), 1989

INTERDEPARTMENTAL COMMITTEE ON THE REDEVELOPMENT OF CONTAMINATED LAND. *Guidance on the assessment and redevelopment of contaminated land.* ICRCL 59/83 (2nd edition). Department of the Environment (London), 1987

INTERDEPARTMENTAL COMMITTEE ON THE REDEVELOPMENT OF CONTAMINATED LAND. *Notes on the restoration and after care of metalliferous mining sites for pasture and grazing.* ICRCL 70/90. Department of the Environment (London), 1990

INTERNATIONAL ORGANISATION FOR STANDARDISATION. *Soil quality – description of soils and sites.* Committee Draft CD 11259

INTERNATIONAL ORGANISATION FOR STANDARDISATION. *Soil quality – sampling: Part 1: Guidance on the design of sampling programmes.* ISO CD 10381-1. Committee Draft (December 1993)

INTERNATIONAL ORGANISATION FOR STANDARDISATION. *Soil quality – sampling: Part 2: Guidance on sampling techniques.* ISO CD 10381-2. Committee Draft (April 1993)

INTERNATIONAL ORGANISATION FOR STANDARDISATION. *Soil quality – sampling: Part 4: Guidance on the procedure for the investigation of natural and near-natural and cultivated soils.* ISO CD 10381-4. Committee Draft (November 1993)

INTERNATIONAL ORGANISATION FOR STANDARDISATION. *Soil quality – sampling: Part 5: Sampling strategies for the investigation of soil contamination of urban and industrial sites.* ISO CD10381. Third draft (September 1993)

INTERNATIONAL ORGANISATION FOR STANDARDISATION. *Soil quality – sampling: Part 5: Guidance on the procedure for the investigation of soil contamination of urban and industrial sites.* ISO CD 10381-5. Committee Draft (October 1993)

INTERNATIONAL ORGANISATION FOR STANDARDISATION. *Soil quality – vocabulary: Part 1: Terms and definitions relating to soil protection and pollution*

INTERNATIONAL ORGANISATION FOR STANDARDISATION/BSI. *General Criteria for the Operation of Testing Laboratories.* BS 7501:1989/EN 45001. BSI (London), 1989

INTERNATIONAL ORGANISATION FOR STANDARDISATION/BSI. *General Criteria for the Assessment of Testing Laboratories.* BS 7502:1989/EN 45002, Guide 25. BSI (London), 1989

INTRON MATERIAL TESTING & CONSULTING. *Opleveringscontrole van Procesmatg Gereinigde Grond en Groundwater [Testing of treated soil and groundwater].* Maastricht, 1986 [in Dutch]

Ionizing Radiation Regulations 1985. HMSO (London), 1985

JACKSON, P.D., MELDRUM, P. and WILLIAMS, G.M. *Principles of a computer controlled multi-electrode resistivity system for automatic data acquisition.* Report WE/89/32. British Geological Survey (Keyworth), 1989

JEFFERIS, S.A. In-ground barriers. In: *Contaminated Land: Problems and Solutions,* T. Cairney (ed.). Blackie (London), 1993, pp 111-140

KEENAN, R.E. *et al.* Taking a risk assessment approach to RCRA corrective action. In *Proceedings of a Conference on Developing Clean-up Standards for Contaminated Soil, Sediment and Groundwater – How Clean is Clean?* Water and Environment Federation (Alexandria VA), 1992, 255-275

KEITH, L.H. *Environmental sampling and analysis: a practical guide.* Lewis Publishers (Chelsea MI), 1991

KEITH, L.H. Throwaway data. *Environmental Science and Technology.* 1994, **28** (8), 389A-390A

KELLY, R.T. Site investigation and material problems. In: *Proceedings of a Conference on the Reclamation of Contaminated Land.* Society of Chemical Industry (London), 1980, pp B2/1-B2/14

LEACH, B.A. AND GOODGER, H.K. *Building on Derelict Land. Special Publication 78.* CIRIA (London), 1991

LORD, D.W. Appropriate site investigations. In: *Reclaiming Contaminated Land,* T. Cairney (ed.), Blackie (Glasgow), 1987, pp 62-113

LOVELL, J. Environmental samples and carefully controlled shipping to prevent degradation. *Pollution Prevention*, June, 1993, 59-61

LUCAS, R.H. and CAIRNEY, T. Reclaiming potentially combustible sites. In: *Contaminated Land – Problems and Solutions*, T. Cairney (ed.). Blackie (London), 1993, pp 141-159

MAUGHAN, J.T. *Ecological Assessment of Hazardous Waste Sites*. Van Nostrand Reinhold (New York), 1993

McCANN, D.M. Geophysical methods for the assessment of landfills and waste disposal sites: a review. *Land Contamination and Reclamation*, 1994, **2** (2), 73-83

McCARTHY, L.S. and MacKAY, D. Enhancing ecotoxicological modelling and assessment. *Environmental Science and Technology*, 1993, **27**, (9), 1714-1725

McFARLAND, R. Simple quantitative risk assessment technique for prioritisation of chemically contaminated sites in New South Wales, Australia. In: *Proceedings of a Conference on Risk Assessment*. Health and Safety Executive (London), 1992

McGRATH, S.P. and LOVELAND, P.J. *The Soil Geochemical Atlas of England and Wales*. Blackie (Glasgow), 1992

Methane investigation strategies. FR/CP/14. CIRIA (London), 1993

MINISTERIE van VOLKSHUISVESTING RUIMTELIJKE ORDENING EN MILEUBEHEER. *Soil protection guideline*. Staatsuitgeverij (s-Gravenhage), 1990

MINISTRY OF AGRICULTURE FISHERIES AND FOOD. *Laboratory methods for work with plant and soil nematodes*. Reference Book 402. HMSO (London), 1986

MINISTRY OF AGRICULTURE FISHERIES AND FOOD. *Sampling of soils, soilless growing media, crop plants and miscellaneous substances for chemical analysis*. MAFF (London), 1979

MINISTRY OF AGRICULTURE, FISHERIES AND FOOD. *The analysis of agricultural materials*. Reference Book 427. HMSO (London), 1985

MINISTRY OF AGRICULTURE, FISHERIES AND FOOD/WELSH OFFICE AGRICULTURE DEPARTMENT. *Code of Good Agricultural Practice for the Protection of Soil*. HMSO (London), 1993

MINISTRY OF HOUSING, PHYSICAL PLANNING AND ENVIRONMENT. *Environmental quality standards for soil and water*. MHPPE/VROM (The Hague), 1991

MINISTRY OF HOUSING, SPATIAL PLANNING AND THE ENVIRONMENT. *Environmental quality objectives in the Netherlands*. (The Hague), 1994

MINISTRY OF HOUSING, SPATIAL PLANNING AND THE ENVIRONMENT. *Soil Protection Act 1994*. (The Hague), 1994

MINISTRY OF THE ENVIRONMENT. *Criteria for managing contaminated sites in British Columbia*. Ministry of the Environment (Victoria, BC), 1989

MOEN, J.E.T. Soil protection in the Netherlands. In: *Proceedings of the Second International TNO/BMFT Conference on Contaminated Soil.* Kluwer (Dordrecht), 1988, pp 1495-1504

MONTGOMERY, R.E., REMETA, D.P. and GRUENFELD, M. Rapid on-site methods of chemical analysis. In: *Contaminated Land: Reclamation and Treatment*, M.A. Smith (ed.). Plenum (London), 1985, pp 257-310

MYERS, K., VOGT, T. and WALES, J. Hazard ranking criteria for contaminated sites. *Land Contamination and Reclamation,* 1994, **2** (1), 13-18

NATIONAL PHYSICAL LABORATORY. *NAMAS Directory of Accredited Laboratories.* NPL (Teddington), 1993

NATIONAL RIVERS AUTHORITY. *Leaching tests for assessment of contaminated land: Interim NRA guidance,* R&D Note 301. NRA (Bristol), 1994

NAYLOR, J.A., ROWLAND, C.D. and BARBER, C. *The investigation of landfill sites.* Technical Report TR 91. WRC (Medmenham), 1978

NEDERLANDS NORMALISATIE-INSTITUUT. *Soil: Investigation Strategy for Exploratory Survey.* NVN 5740. NNI (Delft), 1991

NIELSEN, D.M. (ed.). *Practical Handbook of Groundwater Monitoring.* Lewis Publishers (Chelsea MI), 1991

O'BRIEN, A.A., STEEDS, J.E. and LAW, G.A. Case study: Investigation of Long Cross and Barracks Lane landfill sites. In: *Proceedings of a Conference on Planning and Engineering of Landfills.* Midlands Geotechnical Society (Birmingham), 1992, pp 31-34

OLIVER, G.B.M. *Quality management in construction: implementation in design services organisations.* Special Publication 88. CIRIA (London), 1992

OLIVER, G.B.M. *Quality management in construction: interpretations of BS 5750 (1987) – 'Quality systems' for the construction industry.* Special Publication 74. CIRIA (London), 1990

PETTS, J, Risk assessment for contaminated sites. In: *Proceedings of a Conference on Site Investigations for Contaminated Sites.* IBC Technical Services (London), 1993, Paper No 1

PETTS, J. *Environmental impact assessment for waste treatment and disposal facilities.* Wiley (Chichester), 1994

PETTS, J. Dealing with contaminated land within a risk management framework. In: *Proceedings Conference on Contaminated Land: Policy, Risk Management and Technology, London 1994.* IBC Technical Services (London), 1994

POLLARD, S.J.T., *et al.* Screening of risk management options for abandoned wood-preserving plant sites in Alberta, Canada. *Canadian Journal of Civil Engineering.*

POULSEN, M.M., *et al.* Approaches to the development of soil and groundwater clean up standards in Denmark. In: *Proceedings of a Conference on Developing Clean-up*

Standards for Contaminated Soil, Sediment and Groundwater: How Clean is Clean?. Water and Environment Federation (Alexandria VA), 1993, pp 93-114

Proceedings of a Conference on Developing Clean-up Standards for Contaminated Soil, Sediment and Groundwater: How Clean is Clean?. Water and Environment Federation (Alexandria VA), 1993

RAYBOULD, J.G., ROWAN, S.P. and BARRY, D.L. *Methane investigation strategies* FR/CP/14. CIRIA (London), 1993

REYNOLDS, J.M. and McCANN, D.M. Geophysical methods for the assessment of land-fill and waste disposal sites. In: *Proceedings of the Second International Conference on Construction on Polluted and Marginal Ground*, Forde, M.C. (ed.). Engineering Technic Press (Edinburgh), 1992

RICHARDS MOOREHEAD & LAING. *An Assessment of the Effectiveness of the Methods and Systems used to Reclaim Contaminated Sites in Wales.* Report for the Welsh Office, 1988

ROBITAILLE, G.E. Quantitative in situ soil gas sampling. In: *Proceedings of the Eighth Annual Waste Testing and Quality Assurance Symposium.* American Chemical Society 1992, pp 2-14

ROYAL COMMISSION ON ENVIRONMENTAL POLLUTION. *Tackling pollution experience and prospects.* Tenth Report. HMSO (London), 1984

ROYAL SOCIETY OF CHEMISTRY/INSTITUTION OF CIVIL ENGINEERS/INSTITUTION OF BIOLOGISTS. (list of contaminated land specialists). RSC (London)

ROYAL SOCIETY STUDY GROUP. *Risk: Analysis, perception and management.* Royal Society (London), 1992

SADGROVE, B.M. *Quality assurance in construction – the present position.* Special Publication 49. CIRIA (London), 1986

SAMSON, R. GREER, C.W. and HAWARI, J. *Demonstration of a new biotreatability protocol to monitor a bioprocess for the treatment of contaminated land.* National Research Council of Canada, Biotechnology Research Institute (Ottawa), 1992

SCG. *Inspection of remediated ground and ground to be remediated on behalf of the SCG (Onderzoek te reinigen grond en gereinigde grond t.b.v. het SCG).* SCG (Netherlands), 1992

SCHMIDT, J. Contaminated land: a Canadian viewpoint. In: *Proceedings of a Conference on Contaminated Land Policy, Regulation and Technology.* Paper No.2. IBC (London), 1991

SHEEHAN, P.J., MILLER, D.R., BUTLER, G.C., and BORDEAU P.H. (ed.) *Effects of pollutants at the ecosystem level.* Wiley (Chichester), 1984

SI 1994 No. 1057, The Surface Waters (River Ecosytem) (Classification) Regulations 1994. HMSO (London) 1994

SIEGRIST, R.L. and JENSSEN, P.D. Evaluation of sampling method effect on volatile organic compound measurements in contaminated soils. *Environmental Science and Technology*, 1990, **24**, 1387-1392

SIMMONS, S.M. (ed.) *Hazardous Waste Measurements*. Lewis Publishers (Chelsea MI), 1990

SINCLAIR, A.J. Statistical analysis of trace element data. In: *Applied Science Trace Elements*, B.E. Davies (ed.). Wiley (Chichester), 1980, pp 131-153

SITE INVESTIGATION STEERING GROUP. *Site investigation in construction 1: Without site investigation ground is a hazard.* Thomas Telford Ltd (London), 1993

SITE INVESTIGATION STEERING GROUP. *Site investigation in construction 2: Planning, procurement and quality management.* Thomas Telford Ltd (London), 1993

SITE INVESTIGATION STEERING GROUP. *Site investigation in construction 3: Specifications for ground investigation.* Thomas Telford Ltd (London), 1993

SITE INVESTIGATION STEERING GROUP. *Site investigation in construction 4: Guidelines for the safe investigation by drilling of landfills and contaminated land.* Thomas Telford (London) 1993

SMITH, M.A. Data analysis and interpretation. In: *Recycling derelict land,* G. Fleming (ed.). Thomas Telford Ltd (London), 1991, pp 88-144

SMITH, M.A. Identification, investigation and assessment of contaminated land. *Water and Environmental Management*, 1991, **5** (6), 616-623

SMITH, M. A. Investigation of contaminated sites: standardisation for investigation, testing and analysis. In: *Proceedings Conference on Contaminated Land Site Investigation (London 1993)*. IBC Technical Services (London), 1993

SMITH, M.A. Safety aspects of waste disposal to landfill. In: *Proceedings of a Conference on Planning and Engineering of Landfills.* Midlands Geotechnical Society (Birmingham), 1992, pp 9-21

SMITH, M. A. Standards for the redevelopment of contaminated land. In: *Proceedings of a Conference on the Reclamation of Contaminated Land.* Society of Chemical Industry (London), 1980, pp B1/1-B1/16

SMITH, M.A. *Contaminated Land: Reclamation and Treatment.* Appendix K. Plenum (London), 1985, pp 407-417

SMITH, M.A. Experiences of the development and application of guidelines for contaminated sites in the United Kingdom. In: *Proceedings of a Conference on Developing Clean-up Standards for Contaminated Soil, Sediment and Groundwater: How Clean is Clean?* Water and Environment Federation (Alexandria VA), 1993, pp 195-204

SMITH, M.A. International study of technologies for cleaning-up contaminated land and groundwater. In: *Proceedings of a Conference LAND REC '88.* Durham County Council (Durham), 1988, pp 259-266

SMITH, M.A. and ELLIS, A.C. An investigation into methods used to assess gasworks sites for reclamation. *Reclamation & Revegetation Research*, 1986, **4**, 183-209

SOCIETY FOR ENVIRONMENTAL GEOCHEMISTRY AND HEALTH. WIXSON, B.G. and DAVIES, B.E. *Lead in soil: recommended guidelines.* Science Reviews (Northwood), 1993

SOUTH AUSTRALIAN HEALTH COMMISSION. *Protocol for the health risk assessment and management of contaminated sites.* SAHC (Adelaide), 1991

SOUTH AUSTRALIAN HEALTH COMMISSION. *The health risk assessment and management of contaminated sites.* SAHC (Adelaide), 1991

Specification and method of measurement for ground investigation. HMSO (London), 1987 (Issued in the names of the Department of Transport, Department of the Environment, Property Services Agency, Scottish Development Department, Welsh Office and the Department of the Environment for Northern Ireland)

STANDING COMMITTEE OF ANALYSTS. *Methods for the examination of waters and associated materials – various titles.* HMSO (London), various dates

STATE OF CALIFORNIA DEPARTMENT OF HEALTH SERVICES. *Technical standard for determination of soil remediation levels.* SCDHS, 1990

STEEDS, J., SHEPHERD, E. and BARRY, D.L. *A guide to safe working practices for contaminated sites.* Report 132. CIRIA (London), 1996

STEGEMANN, J.A. and COTE, P.L. *Investigation of Test Methods for Solidified Waste Evaluation – A Cooperative Program.* Report EPS 3/HA/8. Wastewater Technology Centre (Burlington, Ontario), 1991

STIEF, K. The long-term effectiveness of remedial measures. In: *Contaminated Land: Reclamation and Treatment*, Smith, M.A. (ed.). Plenum (London), 1985, pp 13-36

SUTER, G.W. (ed.) *Ecological Risk Assessment.* Lewis Publishers (BOCA Raton, FL) 1993

SUTER, G.W. and LOAR, J.M. Weighing the ecological risk of hazardous waste sites. *Environmental Science and Technology*, 1992, **26** (3), 432-438

TANAKA, J.C. Soil vapour extraction system: Verona Well Field Superfund Site, Battle Creek, Michigan USA. In: *Proceedings of the First International NATO/CCMS Conference on Demonstration of Remedial Action Technologies for Contaminated Land and Groundwater (Washington DC).* USEPA (Cincinnati), 1987, pp 182-187

TAYLOR, L. Laboratory analysis techniques surveyed. *Pollution Prevention*, 1993, **3**, (5), 56-58

THE BRITISH GEOTECHNICAL SOCIETY. *The Geotechnical Directory of the United Kingdom.* Third edition. BGS (London), 1982

THE GEOLOGICAL SOCIETY. *The Geologist's Directory.* Seventh edition. The Geological Society (London), 1994

TILL, J.E. and MOORE, R.E. A pathway analysis approach for determining acceptable levels of contamination of radionuclides in soil. *Health Physics*, **55** (3), 1988, 541-548

TRAVES, L. Applying risk assessment concepts to evaluate alternative uses of contaminated industrial properties. In: *Proceedings of a Conference on Decommissioning, Decontamination and Demolition: Closure of Factory Sites.* Paper No. 4. IBC (London), 1992

UFF, J.F. and CLAYTON, C.R.I. *Recommendations for the procurement of ground investigation.* Special Publication 45. CIRIA (London), 1986

UFF, J.F. and CLAYTON, C.R.I. *Role and Responsibility in Site Investigation.* Special Publication 73. CIRIA (London), 1991

UNICHIM. *Soil analysis, Part I: Manual methods.* Manuele N.145, English edition. UNICHIM (Italian Association for Standardisation in the Chemical Industry) (Milan), 1991

UNICHIM. *Soil analysis, Part II: Semiautomatic methods.* Manuele N.145, English edition. UNICHIM (Italian Association for Standardisation in the Chemical Industry) (Milan), 1991

UNITED STATES ENVIRONMENTAL PROTECTION AGENCY. *CF Systems Organics Extraction System, New Bedford, Massachusetts.* Technology Evaluation Report, EPA/540/5 90/002. USEPA Risk Reduction Engineering Laboratory (Cincinnati), 1990

UNITED STATES ENVIRONMENTAL PROTECTION AGENCY. *Chemfix Technologies Inc. Solidification/Stabilization Process, Clackamas, Oregon.* Technology Evaluation Report, Volume I, EPA/540/5 89/011a. USEPA Risk Reduction Engineering Laboratory (Cincinnati), 1989

UNITED STATES ENVIRONMENTAL PROTECTION AGENCY. *Environmental assessment: Short-term tests for carcinogens, mutagens and other genotoxic agents.* EPA/625/9-79/003. USEPA Health Effects Research Laboratory (Research Triangle Park NC) 1979

UNITED STATES ENVIRONMENTAL PROTECTION AGENCY. *Guidance document for cleanup of surface tank and drum sites.* OSWER Directive 9380.0-3. USEPA (Washington DC), 1985

UNITED STATES ENVIRONMENTAL PROTECTION AGENCY. *Handbook of suggested practices for the design and installation of ground-water monitoring wells.* EPA/600/4-89/034. USEPA (Washington DC), 1991

UNITED STATES ENVIRONMENTAL PROTECTION AGENCY. *Handbook: Groundwater Volume II.* EPA/625/6-90/016b. USEPA (Washington, DC), 1991

UNITED STATES ENVIRONMENTAL PROTECTION AGENCY. *Risk assessment guidance for Superfund, Volume I: Human health evaluation manual (Part A).* EPA/540/1-89/002. USEPA Office of Emergency and Remedial Response (Washington DC), 1989

UNITED STATES ENVIRONMENTAL PROTECTION AGENCY. *Risk assessment guidance for Superfund, Volume II: Environmental evaluation manual.* EPA/540/1-89/001. USEPA Office of Emergency and Remedial Response (Washington DC), 1989

UNITED STATES ENVIRONMENTAL PROTECTION AGENCY. *Risk assessment, management, and communication of drinking water contamination.* EPA/625/4-89/024. USEPA Office of Water (Washington DC), 1989

UNITED STATES ENVIRONMENTAL PROTECTION AGENCY. *Site Program Demonstration of the Ultrox International Ultraviolet Radiation/Oxidation Technology.* Technology Evaluation Report, EPA/540/5 89/012. USEPA Risk Reduction Engineering Laboratory (Cincinnati), 1989

UNITED STATES ENVIRONMENTAL PROTECTION AGENCY. *Site Program Demonstration Test – The American Combustion Pyreton Thermal Destruction System at the US EPA's Combustion Research Facility.* Technology Evaluation Report, EPA/540/5 89/008. USEPA Risk Reduction Engineering Laboratory (Cincinnati), 1989

UNITED STATES ENVIRONMENTAL PROTECTION AGENCY. *Site Program Demonstration Test: Terra Vac In Situ Vacuum Extraction System, Groveland, Massachusetts.* Technology Evaluation Report, Volume I, EPA/540/5 89/003a. USEPA Risk Reduction Engineering Laboratory (Cincinnati), 1989

UNITED STATES ENVIRONMENTAL PROTECTION AGENCY. *Site Program Demonstration Test: Shirco Pilot-scale Infrared Incineration System at the Rose Township Demode Road Superfund Site.* Technology Evaluation Report, EPA/540/5 89/007a. USEPA Risk Reduction Engineering Laboratory (Cincinnati), 1989

UNITED STATES ENVIRONMENTAL PROTECTION AGENCY. Soil treatment by vacuum extraction at Verona Well Field. In: *Proceedings of the Second International NATO/CCMS Conference on Demonstration of Remedial Action Technologies for Contaminated Land and Groundwater (Bilthoven).* USEPA (Cincinnati), 1988, pp 217-240

UNITED STATES ENVIRONMENTAL PROTECTION AGENCY. *State-of-the-art procedures and equipment for internal inspection of underground storage tanks.* EPA/600/2-90/061. USEPA (Washington DC), 1991,

UNITED STATES ENVIRONMENTAL PROTECTION AGENCY. *The risk assessment guidelines of 1984.* EPA/600/8-87/045. USEPA Office of Health and Environmental Assessment (Washington DC), 1987

URLINGS, L.G.C.M. *et al.* In situ cadmium removal. *Final Report NATO Committee on the Challenges of Modern Society Pilot Study: Demonstration of Remedial Action Technologies for Contaminated Land and Groundwater, Volume 1.* EPA/600/R-93/012a. USEPA Risk Reduction Engineering Laboratory (Cincinnati), 1993, pp 1135-1156

URLINGS, L.G.C.M., COFFA, S. and van VREE, H.B.R.T. In situ vapour extraction. In: *Proceedings of the Fourth International NATO/CCMS Conference on Demonstration of Remedial Action Technologies for Contaminated Land and Groundwater (Angers).* USEPA (Cincinnati), 1990

US DEPARTMENT OF HEALTH AND HUMAN SERVICES. *Occupational safety and health guidance manual for hazardous waste site activities.* National Institute for Occupational Safety and Health (Cincinnati), 1985

US ENVIRONMENTAL PROTECTION AGENCY *et al. Proceedings of the Second International Symposium 'Field screening methods for hazardous wastes and toxic chemicals'.* USEPA (Las Vegas), 1991

US ENVIRONMENTAL PROTECTION AGENCY. *Ecological assessments of hazardous waste sites: A field and laboratory reference document.* EPA/600/3-89/013. USEPA Office of Emergency and Remedial Response (Washington DC), 1989

US ENVIRONMENTAL PROTECTION AGENCY. *Framework for ecological risk assessment.* EPA/630/R-92/001. USEPA Risk Assessment Forum (Washington DC), 1992

US ENVIRONMENTAL PROTECTION AGENCY. *Protection EPA – State Soil Standards Conference.* EPA 1540/R-92/005. USEPA (Washington DC), 1992

US ENVIRONMENTAL PROTECTION AGENCY. *Risk assessment guidance for Superfund, Volume II: Environmental evaluation manual.* EPA/540/1-89/001. USEPA Office of Emergency and Remedial Response (Washington DC), 1989

US ENVIRONMENTAL PROTECTION AGENCY. *Standard Operating Safety Guides.* USEPA (Washington DC), 1988

VEGTER, J.J. Developments of soil and groundwater clean-up standards in the Netherlands. In: *Proceedings of a Conference on Developing Clean-up Standards for Contaminated Soil, Sediment and Groundwater: How Clean is Clean?* Water and Environment Federation (Alexandria VA), 1993, pp 81-92

VIELLENAVE J.H. and HICKEY J.C. Use of high resolution passive soil gas analysis to characterize sites contaminated with unknowns, complex mixtures, and semivolatile organic compounds. *Hazardous Materials Control,* 1991, **4** (4), 42-49

WALKER, P.L., MUNRO, S., HAWKINGS, C.L, and SHEPHARD, F.E. A proactive approach to managing an inherited problem – the application of risk assessment to contaminated land. In: *Preprints Symposium on Contaminated Land: From Liability to Asset,* Birmingham, 1994, pp 1-16. Institution of Water and Environmental Management (London), 1994

WATER ENVIRONMENT FEDERATION. *Application of ecological risk assessment to hazardous waste site remediation.* Water Environment Federation (Alexandria VA, USA), 1993

WATER RESEARCH CENTRE/NATIONAL RIVERS AUTHORITY. *Pollution potential of contaminated sites: a review.* R & D Note 181. WRC (Medmenham), 1993

WATSON, C. (ed.) *Official and standardized methods of analysis* (3rd edition). Royal Society of Chemistry (London), 1994

WEELS, S. and CALDWELL, S. Overview of the revised Hazard Ranking System (HRS). In: *Proceedings Superfund '90 Conference, Washington 1990.* Hazardous Materials Research Institute (Silver Spring, MD), 1990, pp 71-76

WELTMAN, A.J. and HEAD, J.M. *Site investigation manual*. Special Publication 25. CIRIA (London), 1983

WILLIAMS, G.M. and JACKSON, P.D. *A multi-electrode system for hydraulic characterisation*. Paper to Hydrogeological Group Meeting of the Geological Society, 'Technical Advances in Downhole Investigation', 1990

YLAND, M.W.F. and SOCZO, E.R. Practical evaluation of a soil treatment plant. *Final Report NATO Committee on the Challenges of Modern Society Pilot Study: Demonstration of Remedial Action Technologies for Contaminated Land and Groundwater, Volume 2 – Part 2*. EPA/600/R-93/012c. USEPA Risk Reduction Engineering Laboratory (Cincinnati), 1993, pp 911-928

YOUNG, P. *Representative groundwater sampling and an overview of surface water sampling, sample handling and storage*. Course notes: Site Investigation, Centre for Extension Studies, Loughborough University, November 1992

INDEX

Note: Numbers in italics refer to Tables. B indicates a Box, and Ap indicates an Appendix

accreditation
    consultants and contractors 34
    NAMAS scheme 171Ap
action values 85, 111
advisers *see* specialists
Advisory Committee on Toxic Substances
    (ACTS) 124B
air
    contaminants in 124-5
    environmental quality standards 114B
air displacement groundwater sampling
    65
air emissions, modelling 212-13Ap
American Petroleum Institute (API),
    guidance documents 155Ap
American Society for the Testing of
    Materials (ASTM) 198Ap
    guidance documents 155Ap
analytical methods, contaminated soils 29
analytical strategies 69-74, 188-98Ap
    environmental analysis 70B
    gasworks contaminants 72B
    off-site laboratories 73
    on-site laboratories 73-4
    on-site measurements 73
    programme scope *70*
    sample preparation *70*
    soil package, typical 71B
Aquacheck, Water Research Centre
    programme 36
aquatic environments 237Ap

aquifers, field evaluation of 180Ap
asbestos 196Ap
asphyxiation, information sources 90B
Association of Environmental
    Consultancies 30, 31, 169Ap
Association of Geotechnical Specialists
    (AGS), guidance documents 34, 155Ap
atmospheres, ambient, sampling 182Ap
atomic absorption, for measurement of
    'total' metals *36*
augering *47*
augers, hollow-stem 173Ap
Australian and New Zealand, guidelines
    and (quality) standards 217Ap

background concentrations
    and contamination 114B, 115
    and remedial values 119
barriers
    horizontal in-ground for containment
        147B, 149
    vertical for containment 147B, 149
Best Available Techniques Not Entailing
    Excessive Cost (BATNEEC) 119
Best Practicable Environmental Option
    (BPEO) 119
bioassays 236ApB
biological assessment, ISO soil sampling
    methods *193*Ap
biological characteristics of substances *88*
biological factors, contaminants and

ecosystems 231ApB
biological surveys 236ApB
black and grey list substances 123B
bladder pumps for groundwater sampling 65
blastfurnace slags, volume stability 196Ap, 198Ap, 198ApB
bleeding 136
boreholes 46-8, *47*
boring, light cable percussive 173Ap
British Columbia, water quality standards 218Ap
British Drilling Association (BDA)
  and ground investigation drillers 169Ap
  guidance documents 155Ap
British Geotechnical Directory, consultant/contractor listing 169Ap
British Research Establishment (BRE), guidance on concrete 121
British Standards Institute (BSI)
  guidance documents 154Ap, 156Ap
  standardised analytical methods 189-90Ap
Building on Derelict Land (CIRIA Special Publication 78) 8
Building Research Establishment (BRE), guidance documents 157Ap

cadmium, soil flushing to remove *142*, 142B, *143*
Canadian Council of Environmental Ministers (CCME), guidance documents 157-8Ap
Canadian criteria/objectives/standards 216-17Ap
carcinogenic hazards 96B
carcinogenicity, information sources 90B
casings, for drilling 175-6Ap
chemical analysis
  ISO methods for soil 192Ap
  and quality assurance 35-7
chemical characteristics of substances *88*
Chemical Industries Association, guidance documents 158Ap
chemical treatment, soil in-situ *140*
Code of Practice for the identification of potentially contaminated land and for its investigation (BSI: DD175:1988) 8
Code of Practice for Site Investigations (BSI: 5930:1981) 154Ap
combustibility, information sources 90B
Comité European de Normalisation (CEN) 188Ap
competitive tendering 28

compliance and performance 129-51
  investigations for *12*, 13
composite samples of soil 19B
concrete, BRE Guidance on sulphate and acid resistance 121
Conditions of Contract for ground Investigation (1983) (ICE) 28
Confederation of British Industry (CBI), guidance documents 158Ap
'Construction (Design and Management) Regulations' (1994) 40
construction, site investigation for 6B
Construction Industry Research and Information Association (CIRIA), guidance documents 158Ap
consultants
  independant inspection of quality systems 34
  information sources on 169Ap
containment methods
  cover systems 146-9
  monitoring 145-9
  vertical/horizontal in-ground barriers 147B, 149
contaminant concentrations 100B
contaminants, possible hypotheses on the distribution of
  heterogeneously distributed 167Ap
  heterogeneously distributed without known point sources 167-8Ap
  homogeneously distributed 167
contaminated sites
  screening factors *102*
  specialists, selection of for investigation 30
contaminated soils
  analytical methods 29
  exposure uptake equation 94B
contamination
  as an investigation objective *10*
  and background concentrations 115
  and biological factors with ecosystems 231ApB
  definition 1, 112-13
  does it exist? 113-14
  does it matter? 115-16
  ecosystems, effect on 225-8Ap, 228ApB
  and the Environmental Protection Act (EPA) (1990) 113B
  evaluation of for ecological planning 233Ap
  hypotheses on spatial distribution of 18
  proving site is uncontaminated 46B
  and site use, information sources

*166*Ap
threshold values 115
and toxicity 229Ap
see also samples/sampling; soil
sampling
contamination related objectives 111
CONTEST scheme 31
contractors
independent inspection of 34
information sources on 169Ap
contracts, *Conditions of Contract for
ground Investigation (1983)* (ICE) 28
Control of Substances Hazardous to
Health (COSHH) (1994),
assessment/regulations 38B, 39
corrosivity, information sources 90B
cover systems
for containment 146-9
inspection/monitoring 147B, *148*
crops, ICRCL Guidelines 121

demonstration projects, evaluation of
remedial methods 151
dense non-aqueous phase liquids
(DNAPLs) 61, *62*
Departments *see* individual names for
departments
desk studies 14-16
information required from 15B
information sources for *165-6*Ap
developers, and hazard ranking 103
*Development Code of Practice (draft) for
the identification of contaminated land
and its investigation* (BSI:
DD175:1988) 154Ap
dioxin in soil, risk assessment 86B
Directory of Environmental Consultants
(ENDs), consultant listing 169Ap
dose, and health risk 201Ap, 208Ap
dose-response relationships 202Ap,
208Ap
and risk assessment 204Ap
drilling
mud-flush and water assisted 174Ap
rotary 173Ap
Drinking Water Directive, and leachate
in ground water 124
drums, sampling 183Ap
Dutch guidelines and standards
ABC values 214ApB
Soil Protection Standards 215ApB

EC directives, surface and groundwater
122-3
ecological assessment 184Ap

for planning 23
ecological epidemiology 238ApB
Ecological risk assessment
application of guidance 221-3Ap
aquatic environments 237ApB,
239ApB
biological factors and contaminants
231ApB
community structure changes 227-8Ap
concepts 222ApB
contaminant evaluation 233Ap
contaminants, effects of 225-30Ap
ecology concepts 225ApB
estimation/evaluation of risks 237-9Ap
framework for *224*Ap
and health assessments *223*Ap
measurement endpoints 234-5Ap
objectives 220-1Ap
planning an assessment 230-7Ap
population size adjustment 227ApB
potential for exposure 233-4Ap
result reporting 240-2Ap
sampling and analysis plan 235-6Ap
site characteristics evaluation 232-3Ap
sources of information 221Ap
spatial considerations 238ApB
temporal considerations 238ApB
ecological risks 203Ap
ecosystems
basic concepts 225ApB
toxicity effects 228ApB
EEC directives, black, grey and red list
substances 123B
effects assessment, for risk estimation 84
employers obligations, for
implementation 27
environment, effects on ecology 230Ap
Environment, Department of
guidance documents 159Ap
Standing Committee of Analysts
190Ap
environmental analysis 70B
environmental evaluation *see* Ecological
risk assessment
environmental hazards, and non-
dedicated guidelines *111*
Environmental Health Departments, local
39
environmental (impact) assessment (EIA)
221Ap
environmental protection
for detailed site investigations *20*
examples of measures 40B
requirements 40
Environmental Protection Act (EPA)

(1990) 113B
environmental quality
  objectives/standards 112
environmental quality standards (EQSs)
  123B
    see also guidelines and (quality)
      standards
evaluation
  remedial methods 150-1
  removal and destruction methods 150-
    1
  versus monitoring 130B
ex-situ treatment *see* treatment processes,
  ex-situ
excavation and material disposal 130,
  131B
expert advice 27-8
    see also specialists
exploratory excavations *20*
exploratory holes, for geotechnical and
  contamination investigation 23
exploratory investigations *12*, 14, 18-19
explosive hazards, and non-dedicated
  guidelines *111*
explosive residues, and sampling 58
explosiveness, information sources 90B
exposure biomarkers 236ApB
exposure and dose
  risk assessment/estimation 84, 92,
    204Ap
  risk quantifying 208Ap

feedstock, monitoring 133
Ferguson conditions, soil sampling 51
fibre-reinforced materials, for
  construction *176*Ap
fill materials 130
fills, Dutch guidelines and standards 214-
  16Ap
fire hazards, and non-dedicated
  guidelines *111*
flammability, information sources 90B
flora and fauna
  macro 195Ap
  sampling 184Ap
fluoropolymer materials, for construction
  *176*Ap
food chains, chemical movement in
  231ApB
free lime hydration, steelmaking slags
  197ApB
Friends of the Earth, guidance documents
  159Ap

gas chromatography 196ApB

gas sampling *47*
gases
  below ground 125
  detection equipment 182Ap
  in-ground 181Ap
  on-site measurements 195Ap
gasworks contaminants 72B
*General criteria for the operation of
  testing laboratories* (EN45001) 35
*General requirements for the technical
  competence of testing laboratories* (ISO
  Guide 25) 35
generic approach to risk assessment 116-
  18
generic standards 118
genetoxic testing 195Ap
Geological Society Directory, consulting
  services 169Ap
geophysical techniques 178Ap
Geotechnical advisers/specialists 31
geotechnics, as an investigation objective
  10, 11B
grab samplers, groundwater sampling *65*
Greater London Council (GLC)
  guidelines 122
Greater London Council (GLC)
  guidelines for contaminants 122
ground investigation, definition 6B
groundwater
  after treatment problems 137-8, *137*
  British Columbia guidelines 218Ap
  Canadian guidelines 217Ap
  contamination of potable 89B
  Dutch guidelines 217Ap
  EC directives 122-3
  ex-situ treatment 131-6
  guidelines for 122
  in-situ treatment 143
  installations for monitoring 34-5
  leachate in 124
  modelling 180Ap
    at a petrol station 211Ap, 212ApB
  on-site measurement 195Ap
  remediation ex-situ treatment
    processes 136-8
groundwater sampling/monitoring *47*
  with bladder pumps *65*
  by air displacement *65*
  by suction lift *65*
  cross contamination 64B
  dense non-aqueous phase liquids
    (DNAPLs) 61, *62*
  device materials 65
  device performances *65*
  drilling methods 173-4Ap

grab samplers *65*
hazardous samples 64B
installation types 62-3, *63*
laboratory measurements 195Ap
mounding of water 61
on-site analysis 64B
phasing investigations 62
pumps, electric submersible *65*
strategies for 60-2
techniques for 63-5, 64B
well purging 64B
guidelines and (quality) standards
　Australian and New Zealand 217Ap
　BRE 121
　British Columbia 218Ap
　Canadian criteria/objectives/standards
　　216-17Ap
　dedicated 109, 110
　definitions and use of 108-9, 118
　documents
　　key 154-5Ap
　　other 155-64Ap
　Dutch 214-16Ap, 217Ap
　generic 118
　GLC 122
　groundwater 122
　ICRCL 120-1
　important terms 112B
　MAFF 121
　non-dedicated 109, 110-11, 117
　remediation use 119
　site specific values 109, 111-12
　surface water 122
　types of 110-12
　UK 120-5
　use for assessment 112-18

hazard, definition 81
hazard acceptability, United States 96B
hazard assessment, using generic
　guidelines *93*
hazard identification/assessment 78, 81B,
　82-4, 91
hazard ranking system 101-3
hazard/pathway/target matrix *92*
hazardous conditions, for site
　investigation 3
hazardous materials *87*
　and health and safety 37
hazardous samples, groundwater
　sampling 64B
hazards, impact on humans 90B
health assessments, and ecological risk
　assessment 221Ap
health hazards, and non-dedicated

guidelines *111*
health risks 82, 82B
　acceptable 209-10Ap
　assessment 201Ap
　combined across exposure pathways
　　209Ap
　dose-response relationships 208Ap
　estimation of 86B
　exposure and dose 208Ap
　from individual substances 209Ap
　from multiple substances 209Ap
　and toxicity 229Ap
health and safety
　safety checklist 38B
　safety procedures *37*
　and site investigation 3, *20*, 37-40, *37*
Health and Safety Executive (HSE)
　consultation with 39
　guidance documents 159-60Ap
　and risk assessment 81
Highways Agency, guidance documents
　160Ap
human health risk *see* health risks
hydrological characteristics, for
　ecological assessment 237ApB
hydrological data 9, 15-16
　information sources *166*Ap
hypotheses development 16-18

in-situ testing *20*
in-situ treatment *see* treatment processes,
　in-situ
Inadequate Site Investigation, ICE report
　5
inductively coupled plasma spectrometry
　36
inorganic analysis 70B
Institute of Petroleum (IP), guidance
　documents 160Ap
Institution of Civil Engineers, guidance
　documents 160Ap
Institution of Environmental Health
　Officers, guidance documents 160Ap
Integrated Pollution Control (IPC) 119
Interdepartmental Committee on the
　Redevelopment of Contaminated Land
　(ICRCL)
　guidance documents 160-1Ap
　guidelines for metalliferous sites 121
　Trigger Concentrations 120-1
International Organisation for
　Standardisation (ISO)
　guidance documents 161Ap
　and soil quality 190-4Ap
investigation procedures/techniques

ambient atmospheres 182Ap
detailed, technical design aspects *20*
detailed investigations 19-21
drums 183Ap
field evaluation of aquifers 180Ap
flora and fauna 184Ap
geophysical techniques 178-9Ap
groundwater modelling 180Ap
groundwater quality 173-7Ap
and health and safety 37-40
in-ground gases 181Ap
integration of 21-3
metallurgical slags 185Ap
micro-organisms 184-5Ap
planning detailed investigations 20-1
radioactivity 182-3Ap
remote sensing 179Ap
for risk assessment 21B
soil valour analysis 177-8Ap
investigation purposes 2-5
investigation services 34
investigations
    detailed 19-21
    exploratory 18-19
    phased *4*, 11-13, *12*
    planning 8-25
    preliminary *12*, 13-18, 14B
Ionizing Radiations Regulations
    (HMSO:1985) 183
iron unsoundness, blastfurnace slags
    198ApB
ISO 9000 34

Laboratory of the Government Chemist
    (LGC) 31
laboratory testing *20*
leachability 135
legal aspects, implementation 27
lime unsoundness, blastfurnace slags
    198ApB
livestock, grazing, ICRCL Guidelines
    121
Loss Prevention Council (LPC), guidance
    documents 162Ap

main investigations *12*
mass spectrometry 196B Ap
metallic materials, for construction
    *176*Ap
metallurgical slags, sampling 185Ap
metals, measurement by digestion and
    atomic absorption or spectrometry *36*
micro-organisms, sampling for 184-5Ap
microbial activity, and vapour extraction
    144B

microbial treatment, soil *140*
mineralogical analysis, for slags 198Ap
mining sites, ICRCL guidelines for
    metalliferous 121
Ministry of Agriculture, Fisheries and
    Food (MAFF), Code of Practice for
    Protection of Soil 121
Ministry of Agriculture and Food 190Ap
Ministry of Housing, Physical Planning
    and Environment (Netherlands),
    guidance documents 162Ap
mixed samples of soil 19B
modelling, for risk assessment 211-13
monitoring
    ex-situ treatment 134-5
    versus evaluation 130B
monitoring equipment *37*
multi-spectral analysis 179Ap
Muskegon, Michigan, case study 98B

National Measurements Accreditation
    Service (NAMAS) 31, 73
    certified laboratory listing 169Ap
    key accreditation elements 171-2Ap
National Rivers Authority in the West
    Midlands 118
Nederlands Normalisatie-Instituut (NNI),
    guidance documents 162Ap
New Jersey Department of Environmental
    Protection (NJDEP), guidance
    documents 162Ap
non-aqueous phases 195Ap
non-carcinogenic hazards 96B

objective setting 8-11, *10*
Occupational Exposure Limits (OELs)
    124B
Occupational Exposure Standards
    (OESs) 124B, 125
off-site laboratories 73
on-site laboratories 73-4
on-site measurements 73
Ontario Ministry of the Environment and
    Energy, guidance documents 162Ap
organic analysis 70B
organic chemicals, classification *88*
organic compounds, background
    concentrations 115
organics, volatile 181Ap
organisms, organisms of 225ApB

pasture for grazing, guidelines for 121
pathways
    as an investigation objective *10*
    critical 101

potential exposure *95*, 98B
    and risk assessment 201Ap
pathways to hazards *87*
performance and compliance 129-51
performance monitoring 33B
periclase hydration
    blastfurnace slags 198ApB
    steelmaking slags 197ApB
peripatetic workers, safety of 39
physical characteristics of substances *88*
phytotoxic effects 121
piezometers, for sampling *47, 62, 63*
pits and trenches for sampling *47*
planning authorities 103
planning investigations 3, 8-25
pollution
    definition 1, 113
    and the Environmental Protection Act
        (EPA) (1990) 113B
populations of organisms 225ApB
    decline from contamination 227ApB
    emigration and immigration 227ApB
post-closure survey 24
post-closure surveys 13
potable groundwater source,
    contamination of 89B
preliminary investigations *12*, 13-18, 14B
probes, driven *47*
procurement
    and competitive tendering 28
    for implementation 27-9
professional advisers 27-8
    see also specialists
professional indemnity insurance 31
project management, implementation 26
protective clothing *37*
pumps, submersible for groundwater
    sampling *65*
purging wells 64B

quality assurance
    for chemical analysis 35
    for containment monitoring 146
    during analysis 198Ap
    of site operations 34-5
quality control, by Water Research Centre
    36
quality management
    chemical analysis 35-7
    environmental protection requirements
        40
    general requirements 32-4
    health and safety 37-40
    long-term sampling and off site works
        40

see also guidelines and (quality)
    standards

radioactivity 196Ap
    testing for 182-3Ap
reconnaissance of sites 16, 17B
red list substances 123B
remedial methods, evaluation 150-1
remedial values 85
remediation, guidelines and standards for
    119
remediation targets 132
remediation values 111
remote sensing, of contaminated sites
    179Ap
remuneration, for procurement 28
reporting, for planning 23-5
risk
    acceptability, United States 96B
    acceptable/unacceptable 115
    common causes of death *202*Ap
    definition 81-2
    qualitative and quantitative 79
    see also Ecological risk assessment;
        health risk; risk assessment
risk assessment
    atmosphere, contaminated *207*Ap
    communication of risks 103-4
    concepts and definitions 80-6, 81B
    conducting a site specific assessment
        91-7
    data quality for 90-1
    of dioxin in soil 86B
    dose-response relationship 204Ap
    exposure 204Ap
    exposure and dose 204Ap
    generic *vs* site-specific quantified 116-
        18
    and ground water modelling 180Ap
    groundwater, contaminated *206*Ap
    human health risk 201Ap
    information requirements 86-91
    investigation procedures for 21B, 22-3
    main uses 80
    modelling air emissions 211Ap
    modelling ground water at a petrol
        station 211Ap, 212ApB
    models, use of 97-9
    objectives and scope 77-80
    pathways 201Ap
    phased investigations and remedies *4*
    and safety 203Ap
    site-specific 78, *79*, 80
    site-specific quantified 117-18
    site-specific value derivation 99, 100B

soils, contaminated *206*Ap
surface water contaminants *205*Ap
toxicity 204Ap, 206Ap
uses of 99-103
see also Ecological risk assessment
risk communication 103-4
risk estimation 78, 81B, 84-5, 92, 98B
risk evaluation 78, 85, 96
risk management 1-2, 77
definition and advantages 1B
risk reduction strategies 77, 100-1
river toxic pollution *226*Ap
rusting, steelmaking slags 197ApB

safety
and risk 203-4Ap
see also health and safety
safety checklist 38B
safety officers 39
safety procedures *37*
samples/sampling
collection of samples *20*, 46-7
drums 183Ap
ex-situ treatment 134
exploration methods *47*
explosive residues 58
flora and fauna 184Ap
gases, in-ground 181Ap
general requirements 48
handling 36-7
and health and safety 37
hypotheses for 45
long term 40
metallurgical slags 185Ap
methods of *47*
for micro-organisms 184-5Ap
patterns and frequencies 45-6
phased sampling *45*
preparation of 36-7
preservation of 29
strategies for 29-30, 45-8
strategy design 45
see also groundwater sampling; soil
sampling; surface water sampling
Scottish Enterprise, guidance documents
163Ap
screening factors, contaminated sites *102*
screens, for drilling 175-6Ap
seals, annular 177Ap
sediment characteristics, for ecological
assessment 237ApB
sediments
Dutch guidelines and standards 214-
16Ap
ex-situ treatment 131-6

selective tendering 28
site characterisation data 86, *88*
site comparison 101-3
site investigation
definition of 6B
see also investigations
Site investigation in construction (Site
Investigation Steering Group) 30
Site investigation manual (CIRIA: SP25)
155Ap
Site Investigation Steering Group 30, 31
guidance documents 163Ap
Site operations, and quality assurance 34-
5
site-specific values, guidelines and
standards 111-12
slags *see* blastfurnace slags; steelmaking
slags
soil sampling
biological assessment, ISO methods
193
character and role of personnel for 50B
chemical/physical analysis 193-5Ap
ISO methods *192*Ap
containers 56, *57*
contamination in trench *59, 60*
contamination variation *58*
DD175 (1988) recommendations 50B
Ferguson conditions 51-5
herringbone sampling pattern *52, 54,
55, 57*
hot spots 51, 52
ISO standards *191*Ap
judgemental sampling 50B
locating to 95confidence 54B
options *49*
patterns and frequency 49-55
procedures for 55-9
regular grid pattern 51, *54, 57*
simple random pattern 51, *54, 57*
standards, organisations producing
*189*Ap
stratified random pattern 51, *52, 54,
57*
types of soil 19B
in typical housing development *53*
and volatile substances 56, *58, 59*
soil vapour analysis 177-8Ap
soil(s)
background and reference values 114B
Dutch guidelines and standards 214-
16Ap
ex-situ treatment 131-6
in-situ treatment 139-42
ISO standards for quality 190-4Ap

MAFF Code of Price for Protection of
121
multi-functionality of 117B
spot samples 19B
specialist service providers 32B
specialists 27
guidance on 169Ap
selection of 30-2, 32B
specifications, site investigations 29-30,
29
spectrometry, inductively coupled plasma
36
stabilisation/solidification processes 133-
6
standards
generic 118
see also guidelines and (quality)
standards
standpipes 47
Statutory Water Quality Objectives 117B
steelmaking slags, volume stability 196-
7Ap, 197ApB
strategy
for groundwater sampling 60-2
for sampling and testing 44-8
for site investigations 3
submersible pumps for groundwater
sampling 65
suction lift groundwater sampling 65
sulphoaluminate formation, blastfurnace
slags 198ApB
Superfund Innovative Technology
Evaluation (SITE) program (US
Environmental Agency) 133
supplementary investigations 12, 13
surface sampling 47
surface water
Canadian guideline values 216Ap
Dutch guideline values 216Ap
EC directives 122-3
environmental quality standards 114B
guidelines for 122
on-site measurement 195Ap
surface water sampling
charerisation of the hydrological
regime 67
chemical testing parameters 67
estuarine waters 67
judgemental/systematic/random
sampling 68
laboratory measurements 195Ap
possible approaches 66, 67
programme requirements 66
sediments 69
static water 69

targets
as an investigation objective 10
definition 82
of hazards 87
Technical Committee 190 (soil quality)
(ISO) 188Ap
terminology, for phases of investigations
12
test laboratories 35
testing see samples/sampling
thermal treatment materials ex-situ 133B
sampling and assessment procedures
for 134B
thermoplastic materials, for construction
176Ap
third party accreditation, consultants and
contractors 34
Thomas Solvent Raymond Road project,
vapour extraction 141B
threshold value of contamination 115
toluene, and vapour extraction 144,
144B, 145
topographical surveys 16
toxic pollution, rivers 226Ap
toxicity
assessment 92
assessment in United States 94B
information sources 90B
and risk assessment 204Ap, 206Ap
testing 195Ap
toxilogical data 89-90
Transport, Department of, guidance
documents 159Ap
travel risks 203Ap
treatment processes, ex-situ
groundwater remediation 136-8
leachability 135
monitoring 134-5
performance assessment 131-3
remediation targets 132
sampling and testing 134
stabilisation/solidification processes
133-6
thermal treatment effectiveness 133B,
134B
treatment processes, in-situ
general considerations 138-9
groundwater/liquid phases 143
proving site is clean 140
soils and similar materials 139-43
testing 139
trigger values, and dedicated guidelines
and standards 110
Trigger Values/Concentrations, ICRCL

120-1

UK Standing Committee of Analysts (SCA) 188Ap
United States
  hazard acceptability 96B
  risk acceptability 96B
  toxicity assessment 94B
US Environmental Protection Agency (USEPA)
  demonstration projects 151
  and ecological risk assessment 221Ap, 222ApB
  guidance documents 81, 163Ap
User Network for Applied Modelling of Air Pollution (UNAMAp) 213Ap

Validity of Analytical Measurements initiative (DTI) 31
vapour extraction
  from soil *140*
  and microbial activity 144B
  Thomas Solvent Raymond Road project 141B
  toluene *144*, 144B, *145*
variability, dealing with 119-20
volatile organic compounds (VOCs) 177Ap, 181Ap
volatile substances, and soil sampling 56, 58, *59*

washing/flushing soil *140*
waste management licences, surrender of 124
Waste Management Paper 26A (Dep. of Env./Scottish Office/Welsh Office) 124, 125
water *see* groundwater; surface water
water analysis
  standard methods for 35-6
  standards, organisations producing *189*Ap
water environment, as an investigation objective *10*
water quality for ecological assessment 237ApB
Water Research Centre 36, 190Ap
waters, multi-functionality of 117B
wells *47*
  development of 177Ap
  purging, groundwater sampling 64B
Welsh Development Agency, guidance documents 163Ap
Working Group on the Assessment of Toxic Chemicals (WATCH) 124B
World Health Organisation Air Quality Guidelines 213Ap

zootoxic effects 121

4 Volume IV Classification and selection of remedial methods (SP104)

Volume IV describes a structured process for the identification, evaluation and screening of remedial methods (and combinations of methods) and the selection of a preferred remedy. Key selection criteria defining the applicability (to specific contaminants and host media), effectiveness (in meeting contamination-related and other remedial objectives), feasibility and costs of the different options are described as an aid to objective selection and evaluation.

A range of generic remedial methods are introduced and a simple classification provided. Two main groups are identified:

1. *Civil-engineering based methods* (including removal (excavation), containment (e.g. vertical barriers, surface covers etc.) and hydraulic measures.
2. *Process-based methods* in which thermal, physical, chemical, biological and stabilisation/solidification processes are used to remove, destroy or modify contaminants. Process-based methods are further differentiated according to the mode of application, e.g. after removal of contaminated material from the ground (ex-situ) or without prior removal of the material (in-situ).

The potential advantages and limitations of the various methods are reviewed.

CONTENTS

1 **INTRODUCTION**
    1.1   Scope and application
    1.2   The selection process
    1.3   Remedial options
    1.4   Environmental policy
    1.5   Structure of the volume
    References

2 **THE SELECTION PROCESS**
    References

3 **REMEDIAL ACTION OBJECTIVES**
    3.1   Purpose and scope
    3.2   Contamination-related objectives
    3.3   Engineering objectives
    3.4   Management objectives
    3.5   Site-specific constraints
    3.6   Prioritising objectives and constraints
    References

4 OPTIONS FOR TREATMENT
4.1   Classification
4.2   Definitions
4.3   The classification system
4.4   Further information
References

5 DEVELOPMENT OF ALTERNATIVE REMEDIAL STRATEGIES
5.1   Scope
5.2   Zoning the site for treatment
5.3   Identification and evaluation of remedial and process options
5.4   Integration of methods
5.5   Evaluation of alternative strategies
5.6   Output of the first stage
References

6 ADDITIONAL DATA COLLECTION
6.1   Scope
6.2   Data requirements
6.3   Treatability studies
6.4   Other data gathering and processing activities
References

7 DETAILED ANALYSIS AND SELECTION OF THE PREFERRED REMEDY
7.1   Scope
7.2   Description of alternative remedial strategies
7.3   Evaluation against key criteria
7.4   Comparative analysis and selection of the preferred remedy

APPENDIX 1 RISK AVOIDANCE
A1.1   Scope
A1.2   Modification of land use
A1.3   Alteration of the site layout
A1.4   Other temporary measures
References

APPENDIX 2 CIVIL ENGINEERING METHODS
A2.1   Description
A2.2   Excavation
A2.3   On-site disposal
A2.4   Covering systems
A2.5   In-ground barriers
A2.6   Hydraulic measures
A2.7   Costs of civil engineering based methods
References

APPENDIX 3 PROCESS-BASED METHODS
A3.1   Description
A3.2   Thermal treatment methods
A3.3   Physical treatment methods
A3.4   Chemical treatment methods
A3.5   Biological treatment methods
A3.6   Stabilisation/solidification methods
A3.7   Costs of process-based methods
References

APPENDIX 4 FACTORS TO BE CONSIDERED DURING SELECTION
A4.1   Applicability
A4.2   Effectiveness
A4.3   Limitations
A4.4   Cost
A4.5   Development status
A4.6   Availability
A4.7   Operational requirements
A4.8   Information requirements
A4.9   Planning and management
A4.10 Monitoring
A4.11 Combination and integration of treatment methods
A4.12 Environmental impact
A4.13 Health and safety
A4.14 Post treatment management
References

REFERENCES

ANON. *Technologie Register zur Zanierung von Altlasten (TERESA)*. Der Bundesminister für Forschung und Technologie (Bonn), 1990

BECKETT, M.J. and SIMMS, D.L. Assessing contaminated land UK policy and practice. In: *Proceedings of the First International TNO Conference on Contaminated Soil*. Martinus Nijhoff Publishers (Dordrecht), 1985, pp 285-293

BEINAT, E. and JANSSEN, R., SOILS: a system to support decisions on cleaning up polluted sites. In: *Integrated soil and sediment research: as basis for proper protection*, H.J.P. Eijsackers and T. Hamers (eds), Kluwer (Dordrecht), 1993, pp 481-484

BISHOP, P.L. Solidification/stabilisation of contaminated soils – an overview. In: *Proceedings of the Third International KfK/TNO Conference on Contaminated Soil (Contaminated Soil '90)*. Kluwer (Dordrecht), 1990, pp 1265-1274

BLAUSTEIN, M. and VOORHEES, P. Using decision analysis to evaluate site remediation costs. *Clayton Environmental Bulletin*, Clayton Environmental Consultants Inc. (Novi MI), 1992, pp 12-13

CAIRNEY, T. Soil cover reclamations. In: *Reclaiming Contaminated Land*, Cairney. T. (ed.). Blackie, (Glasgow), 1987

CAIRNEY, T. Theory and practice of soil cover system design. In: *Proceedings of a Conference on Contaminated Land Policy, Regulation and Technology*. Paper No. 13. IBC (London), 1992

CHILDS, K. Management and treatment of groundwater. In: *Contaminated Land*, Smith, M.A. (ed.). Plenum Press (New York), 1985

DE BRUIJN, P. Bio-treatment in soil remediation. In: *Proceedings of a Conference on Contaminated Land: Policy, Regulation and Technology*. Paper No 11. IBC (London), 1992

DEPARTMENT OF ENVIRONMENT. *Evaluation of Derelict Land Schemes.* HMSO (London), 1987

DEPARTMENT OF HEALTH. Evidence to the House of Commons Environment Committee Inquiry on Contaminated Land, Volume III Appendices. 1990, pp 296-297

DEPARTMENT OF THE ENVIRONMENT. *Guidance for evaluating the performance of remedial methods for contaminated land.* DoE (London)

DEPARTMENT OF THE ENVIRONMENT/WELSH OFFICE. *Environmental Assessment: A guide to the procedures,* HMSO (London), 1989

DEPARTMENT OF THE ENVIRONMENT. *Cost effective management of reclaimed derelict sites.* HMSO (London), 1989

DEPARTMENT OF THE ENVIRONMENT. *Evaluation of derelict land grant schemes.* HMSO (London), 1987

DEPARTMENT OF THE ENVIRONMENT. *Landfilling wastes* (WMP26). A Technical Memorandum for the disposal of wastes on landfill sites. HMSO (London), 1986

HARRIS, M.R. Land remediation technologies: A techno-economic appraisal. In: *Paper presented to Cycle de Conferences sur l'Environnement.* Société Royale Belge des Ingenieurs et des Industrials (Brussels), March 1991

HEALTH AND SAFETY EXECUTIVE. *Protection of workers and the general public during the development of contaminated land.* HS (G) 66. HMSO (London), 1991

HINSENVELD, M. *et al.* Alternative physico-chemical and thermal cleaning technologies for contaminated soil. In: *Proceedings of the Third International KfK/TNO Conference on Contaminated Soil (Contaminated Soil '90).* Kluwer (Dordrecht), 1990, pp 873-881

LORD, A. Options available for problem solving. In: *Recycling Derelict Land,* Fleming, G. (ed.). Thomas Telford Ltd (London), 1991

NATIONAL INSTITUTE FOR PUBLIC HEALTH AND ENVIRONMENTAL HYGIENE OF THE NETHERLANDS and FREE UNIVERSITY OF AMSTERDAM, *Development of a decision support system for cleaning up polluted sites.* Interim Report project 8988. RIVM/IvM/VU (Bilthoven), 1993

PARSONS, L.S., WATERMAN, L. *A guide to the control of substances hazardous to health in construction.* Report 125. CIRIA (London), 1993

ROYAL COMMISSION ON ENVIRONMENTAL POLLUTION. *Best Practicable Environmental Option.* Twelfth Report. HMSO (London), 1988

SIMS, R.C. Soil remediation techniques at uncontrolled hazardous waste sites. A critical review. *J. Air Waste Management Association,* May 1990, Vol 40 (No.5), 704-732

SMITH, M.A. Available reclamation methods. In: *Reclaiming Contaminated Land,* Cairney, T. ed.). Blackie (Glasgow), 1987, pp 114-143

SMITH, M.A. Contamination and the environment. In: *Proceedings of a Seminar on Policy Analysis for Housing and Planning*. PTRC Summer Meeting, Warwick, 1982. PTRC (London), 1982

SMITH, M.A., Dealing with contaminated ground conditions. *Land contamination and reclamation*, 1993, 1 (1) 22 22-36

SMITH, M.A. Options and criteria for the remediation of contaminated sites. In: *Proceedings of a Conference on Contaminated Land: Policy, Regulation and Technology*. IBC Technical Services (London), 1990

SMITH, M.A., The 'engineer' and contaminated land. *Structural Engineer*, 1982, 60A(1), 5-8

STEEDS, J.E., SHEPHERD, E. and BARRY, D.L. *A guide to safe working practices for contaminated sites*. Report 132. CIRIA (London), 1996

STINSON, M.K. *et al* EPA SITE Demonstration of the BioTrol soil washing process. *J. Air Waste Management Association. January 1990, Vol 42, (No 1), 97-103*

TACIUK, W. Thermal processes – recovery of hydrocarbons through anaerobic pyrolysis using the AOSTRA-Taciuk processor. In: *Proceedings of the Second Annual Conference on Clean-up of Contaminated Sites*. Toronto, 1992

UNITED STATES ENVIRONMENTAL PROTECTION AGENCY. *Alternative Treatment Technology Information Center (ATTIC) Database*. USEPA (on-line source)

UNITED STATES ENVIRONMENTAL PROTECTION AGENCY. *Babcock & Wilcox Cyclone Furnace vitrification technology*. Applications Analysis Report, EPA/540/AR-92/017. USEPA Office of Research and Development (Washington DC), 1992

UNITED STATES ENVIRONMENTAL PROTECTION AGENCY. *Bioremediation in the field*. EPA/540/2-91/018. USEPA Office of Solid Waste and Emergency Response, Office of Research and Development (No.3) (Washington DC), August 1991

UNITED STATES ENVIRONMENTAL PROTECTION AGENCY. *BioTrol soil washing system for treatment of a wood preserving site*. Application Analysis Report, EPA/540/A5-91/003. USEPA Office of Research and Development (Washington DC), 1992

UNITED STATES ENVIRONMENTAL PROTECTION AGENCY. *CF Systems organics extraction process, New Bedford Harbour, MA*. Applications Analysis Report, EPA/540/A5-90/002. USEPA Office of Research and Development (Washington DC), 1990

UNITED STATES ENVIRONMENTAL PROTECTION AGENCY. *Demonstration of remedial action technologies for contaminated land and groundwater*. Final Report of NATO/CCMS Pilot Study, EPA/600/R-93/012 a,b,c. USEPA (Cincinnati), 1993

UNITED STATES ENVIRONMENTAL PROTECTION AGENCY. *Guidance for conducting remedial investigations and feasibility studies under CERCLA*. Interim Final Report, EPA/540/G-89/004. USEPA Office of Emergency and Remedial Response (Washington DC), 1989

UNITED STATES ENVIRONMENTAL PROTECTION AGENCY. *Guide for conducting treatability studies under CERCLA*. Final Report, EPA/540/R-92/07a. USEPA Office of Research and Development, Office of Solid Waste and Emergency Response (Washington DC), 1992

UNITED STATES ENVIRONMENTAL PROTECTION AGENCY. *Innovative treatment technologies: Overview and guide to information sources*. EPA/540/9-91/002. USEPA Office of Solid Waste and Emergency Response (Washington DC), 1991

UNITED STATES ENVIRONMENTAL PROTECTION AGENCY. *Remediation of contaminated sediments*. EPA/625/6-91/028. USEPA Office of Research and Development (Washington DC), 1991

UNITED STATES ENVIRONMENTAL PROTECTION AGENCY. *RREL Treatability database*. USEPA Risk Reduction Engineering Laboratory, Office of Research and Development (on-line source)

UNITED STATES ENVIRONMENTAL PROTECTION AGENCY. *Soliditech Inc. solidification/stabilisation process*. Application Analysis Report, EPA/540/A5-89/005. USEPA Office of Research and Development (Washington DC), 1990

UNITED STATES ENVIRONMENTAL PROTECTION AGENCY. *Terra Vac in situ vacuum extraction system*. Applications Analysis Report, EPA/540/A5-89/003. USEPA Office of Research and Development (Washington DC), 1989

UNITED STATES ENVIRONMENTAL PROTECTION AGENCY. *The Superfund Innovative Technology Evaluation Programme Technology Profiles*. Sixth edition, EPA/540/R-93/526. USEPA Office of Solid Waste and Emergency Response, Office of Research and Development (Washington DC), 1992

UNITED STATES ENVIRONMENTAL PROTECTION AGENCY. *The Superfund Innovative Technology Evaluation Programme Technology Profiles*. Fifth edition, EPA/540/R-92/077. USEPA Office of Solid Waste and Emergency Response (Washington DC), 1992

UNITED STATES ENVIRONMENTAL PROTECTION AGENCY. *Toxic Treatments in-situ steam/hot-air stripping technology*. Application Analysis Report, EPA/540/A5-91 003. USEPA Office of Research and Development (Washington DC), 1992

UNITED STATES ENVIRONMENTAL PROTECTION AGENCY. *Vendor Information System for Innovative Treatment Technologies (VISITT)*. USEPA Technology Information Office (diskettes)

WARREN SPRING LABORATORY. *Review of innovative contaminated soil clean-up processes*. WSL (Stevenage), 1992

INDEX

Note: Numbers in italics refer to Tables. B indicates a Box, and Ap indicates an Appendix

affected media, chemical/physical
  characteristics, information required
  *69*Ap
air monitoring 70Ap
alternative remedial strategies 22-30
  assessment using key criteria 37-40
  comparative analysis and selection of
    preferred remedy 41
  descriptive information 36-7
  development of 5
  evaluation of 29
  identification/evaluation of
    remedial/process options 23-5
  integration of methods 27, *28*
  zoning site for treatment 23

barriers, excavated 48Ap
Best Practical Environmental Option
  (BPEO) 3, 5
biological degradation routes 56Ap
biological treatment 27B, 56Ap, 71Ap
  aerobic and anaerobic 56Ap
  potential advantages and constraints
    57ApB
bioremediation
  in-situ, testing and monitoring of 70-
    1Ap
  indicative costs *64*Ap
building services, installation within
  cover layer 47Ap

chemical barriers 48Ap
chemical reagents 56ApB
  use of 55Ap
chemical treatment methods 55Ap
  potential advantages and constraints
    56ApB
civil engineering methods 12, 45-51Ap
  classification of 14, *15*
  costs of 50-1Ap
  covering systems 47-8Ap, 48ApB
  excavation 45, 46B
  hydraulic measures 49-50Ap, 50ApB
  in-ground barriers 48-9Ap, 49ApB
containment systems
  decline in effectiveness of 63Ap
  see also in-ground barriers
contaminants
  characteristics of, information required
    *69*Ap

levels of 8
  migration, potential threat of 9
  treatment on-site 2
  'untreated', remaining on site 37
contaminated land/sites
  crossed by new road and sewer
    developments 43Ap
  suitable uses for 43Ap
contaminated liquids
  chemical treatment of 55Ap
  and solids, remedial treatment methods
    14, *19-21*
contamination
  and civil engineering costs 51Ap
  constraints on engineering objectives 9
  residual, permitted level of 9
contamination-related objectives
  qualitative 8-9
  quantitative 9
control methods/technologies, adequacy
  and reliability of 37-8, *38*
controlled waste, keeping or disposal of
  46Ap
cost elements, compared, uncontaminated
  and contaminated sites *65*Ap
cost pressures, different, public and
  private sector projects 64-5Ap
cost sensitivity analysis, key elements
  66Ap, 66ApB
costs 63-7Ap, *69*Ap
  of alternative remediation strategies
    29, 39-40, *40*
  of civil engineering methods 50-1Ap
  estimation of 66-7Ap
  of process-based methods 58-60Ap
    care needed in cost comparisons 59
costs, risks and effectiveness, balancing
  of 29
covering systems 47-8Ap, 51Ap
  potential advantages and constraints
    48ApB
  requirements of 47Ap
  for site encapsulation with other
    methods 47Ap
critical exposure route(s)and target(s) 8

data
  additional
    collection of *5*, 31-4
    gathered on pre-design basis 34

site-based, collection of 23
   information requirements for selection
      process 69-70Ap
dechlorination 55Ap
Department of the Environment 51Ap
Derelict Land Grant system/programme
   51Ap, 65Ap
derelict sites, reclamation to 'soft' uses
   51Ap
displacement systems 48Ap

effectiveness
   of a remediation measure 62-3Ap
   variation over time 63Ap
electrokinetic techniques (*in-situ*),
   indicative costs *64*Ap
engineering objectives, of remedial
   actions 9
Environment, Department of 51Ap
environmental impacts 38, 71Ap
   secondary 3
environmental policy, influence on
   selection and application of remedial
   methods 2-3
environmental protection
   monitoring for 70Ap
   requirements 34
evaluation, of options against criteria 7
excavated barriers 48Ap
excavated material, treatment at licensed
   facility 45Ap
excavation 45-6Ap, 72Ap
   and off-site disposal, indicative costs
      *64*Ap
   potential advantages and constraints
      46ApB
exhaust gases, treatment of 53Ap

goods and services, potential availability
   of 70Ap
groundwater
   contaminated, use of hydraulic
      containment measures 50
   and other liquids, contaminated,
      process-based treatment methods *21*

hazardous materials, potential,
   requirements for health and safety
   provisions 71-2Ap
health and safety 71-2Ap
   compliance monitoring 70Ap
   requirements 34
   of workforce 38
hydraulic measures 49-50Ap
   potential advantages and constraints
      50ApB
hydrolysis 55Ap

implementation costs 39, *40*
in-ground barriers 48-9Ap
   horizontal, different approaches 49Ap
   potential barriers and constraints
      49ApB
   vertical 48ApB
incineration 53Ap, 67Ap
injection barriers 48Ap

laboratory testing 23
land use, modification of and risk
   avoidance 42-3Ap
landfill, and on-site disposal 46-7Ap
legal obligations 8
limitations, constraining remediation
   measures 63Ap
literature survey, for further data
   requirements 31
long-term performance and permanence
   37-8
low cost immediate solutions, pressure for
   65Ap

management
   information requirements for selection
      process *69*Ap
   of remedial strategies *39*
management factors, influencing costs
   67Ap
management objectives, remedial actions
   9-10
managerial feasibility, of alternative
   strategies 29
monitoring 70-1Ap

NATO/CCMS programme 67Ap
New Bedford Harbor, Mass., methods and
   processes considered for remediation of
   contaminated sediments 25, *26*

objectives and constraints, prioritising of
   11
off-site disposal 27B, 45Ap
on-site disposal 45Ap, 46-7Ap
   conforming to good practice for
      landfilling 46-7Ap
   potential advantages and constraints
      47ApB
operational requirements 68-9Ap
oxidation-reduction 55Ap

particulate separation techniques 54Ap

permanence, of remedial strategies 37
pH adjustment 55Ap
phenol-contaminated site, development of
   alternative remediation strategies 27B
physical barriers, temporary 48Ap
physical treatment methods 54-5Ap
   potential advantages and constraints
      55ApB
pilot plants
   installation and start-up 34
   operation and maintenance procedures
      34
pilot-scale test programmes 33, 34, 35
planning and management 70Ap
pollution, control of 2
post-implementation costs 40, 40
post-treatment, a management objective
   10B
post-treatment management, short and
   long-term measures needed 71-2Ap
post-treatment management controls 37,
   43Ap
pre-implementation costs 39, 40
process control and optimisation,
   monitoring for 70Ap
process options, identification and
   evaluation of 23-5
process-based methods 12, 52-60Ap
   biological treatment methods 56Ap,
      57ApB
   can be applied *in-situ* and *ex-situ* 52Ap
   chemical treatment methods 55Ap,
      56ApB
   classification of 14, 18
      ex-situ methods 14, 16, 19
      in-situ methods 14, 17, 20
   costs of 58-60Ap
   physical treatment methods 54-5Ap,
      55ApB
   stabilisation/solidification methods
      57Ap, 58ApB
   thermal treatment methods 53Ap,
      54ApB
protection and compliance 37
public health 38

quality management systems 70Ap

regulatory authorities, in setting remedial
   action objectives 8
regulatory requirements 37
remedial action(s) 8-11
   contamination-related objectives 8-9
   engineering objectives 9
   impacts during implementation 38

management objectives 9-10
practical aspects of implementation 38-
   9, 39
prioritising objectives and constraints
   11
purpose and scope 8
site-specific constraints 10, 10B
remedial costs, comparison with doing
   nothing 65Ap
remedial options 2
   factors affecting numbers of 22
remedial strategy, preferred, case for
   prepared with care 41
remedial system, implications of failure
   in 37-8
remedial/remediation methods 24
   availability of 68Ap
   combination and integration of 71Ap
   development status of 67-8Ap
   information requirements 69-70Ap
   integration of 27
   operational requirements 68-9Ap
   posing additional and specific health
      and safety hazards 71-2Ap
   practicalities of implementation 25
   preliminary screening 1
   and process options, identification and
      evaluation of 23-5
   proven or innovative 68-7Ap
   selected, operational and performance
      data required 69Ap
   some additional data requirements 32
remediation
   availability of funds 64Ap
   detailed analysis and selection of
      preferred remedy 36-41
   division of area into smaller units 11
   main stages in 1
   a management objective 10B
remediation strategies
   common cost elements 39-40, 40
   institutional acceptance 40
   social and community impact and
      acceptance 40
residual risk 37, 38
risk assessment 7
   and alteration of site layout 43Ap
   and site investigation, information
      from 70Ap
risk avoidance 42-4Ap
   alteration of site layout 43Ap
   measures for 2
   modification of land use 42-3Ap
   use of temporary measures 43-4Ap
   where not applicable 42Ap

risk reduction
   measures for 2
   through effective remediation 62Ap

sampling and laboratory analysis 70Ap
sampling plans, treatability testing 34
screening, of promising strategies 7
secondary emissions, need for collection
  and treatment 2
selection process 1-2, 5-7
   basic steps 5
   factors for consideration during 62Ap
   first stage, purpose of 22
   key factors for initial selection 23B
   need for additional data 31
   output of first stage 29
   second stage, key criteria 36-41
sensitivity, of land uses 42-3Ap
services and materials, practicality of
  provision of *39*
site-specific limitations 63Ap
sites
   characteristics of, information required
    *69*Ap
   layout and risk avoidance 43Ap
   zoning, with and without hot spots 23,
    24
social costs 67Ap
soil, problems of incineration 53Ap
soil, sludges and sediments, process-
  based treatment methods *19-20*
soil vapour extraction (*in-situ*), indicative
  costs *64*Ap
soil washing
   indicative costs *64*Ap
   processes 9
   systems 54Ap
solvent extraction systems 54Ap, 72Ap
stabilisation/solidification methods 57Ap
  58ApB 67Ap, 71Ap
   indicative costs *64*Ap
stakeholders, views must be taken into
  account 65Ap
supplementary site investigation 31

technical feasibility
   of alternative strategies 29
   of implementation *39*

technical sufficiency, of alternative
  strategies 38
thermal desorption 53Ap
thermal treatment 9, 53Ap, 72Ap
   anaerobic, costs of 60ApB
   indicative costs *64*Ap
   potential advantages and constraints
    54ApB
treatability studies 31-4
   at bench-scale and pilot scale 32, 33,
    33
   need for 31-2
   objectives of 33-4
    test programme 33-4
treatability tests, a form of pre-design 34
treated material, changes in engineering
  properties of 9
treatment 12
treatment options 12-14, *15-21*
   classification of 12, *13*, 14
treatment residues, and residual risk 37

uncertainty, through failure to specify
  propose site after-use 8
US Environmental Protection Agency
  (USEPA)
   costs of process-based methods 58ApB
   protocols 5
   recognition of reliable technologies
    67Ap, *67*Ap
   Superfund Innovative Technology
    Evaluation (SITE) Programme 67Ap

vitrification 53Ap

waste
   controlled, keeping or disposal of
    46Ap
   minimisation of at source 2
waste management license, necessity for
  46Ap
waste management requirements 34
Waste Regulation Authority, compliance
  with requirements of 70Ap
waste streams, from remediation 71Ap
work plan, treatability testing 34, *35*
   key elements of *35*

5 Volume V Excavation and disposal (SP105)

Volume V is the first of five dealing with specific groups of remediation methods. Excavation is considered as a unit process preceding the disposal (on or off-site) or further treatment (in a process-based system) of contaminated material.

The technique is reviewed in terms of applicability, limitations, effectiveness, practical requirements and costs. The technical, administrative and legal implications of both on and off-site disposal options are also addressed.

CONTENTS

1 **INTRODUCTION**
    1.1   Excavation and off-site disposal
    1.2   Excavation and on-site disposal
    1.3   Information requirements
    1.4   Applicability of the guidance
    References

2 **GENERAL DESCRIPTION**
    2.1   Objectives
    2.2   Applicability
    2.3   Description
    2.4   Boundary definition
    2.5   Preparatory works
    2.6   Excavation
    2.7   Materials handling
    2.8   Off-site disposal
    2.9   On-site disposal
    2.10   Post-treatment validation
    2.11   Materials replacement
    2.12   Integration with other remedial methods
    2.13   Ancillary measures
    References

3 **OPERATIONAL REQUIREMENTS**
    3.1   Definition
    3.2   Legislation and approvals
    3.3   Site requirements
    3.4   Plant and equipment
    3.5   Laboratory support
    3.6   Personnel needs
    References

4 PLANNING AND MANAGEMENT

4.1   Planning
4.2   Specification
4.3   Contractual arrangements
4.4   Procurement
4.5   Supervision
References

5 PERFORMANCE

5.1   Remedial action objectives
5.2   Ability to meet other objectives
5.3   Limitations
5.4   Proven applications
References

6 COST OF THE METHOD

6.1   Introduction
6.2   Typical cost breakdown
6.3   Typical costs

7 PROGNOSIS

Appendix 1   Examples of the information to be provided in a safety plan for excavation operations

REFERENCES

BRITISH STANDARDS INSTITUTION. *Code of Practice for Earthworks,* BS 6031. BSI (London), 1981

BRITISH STANDARDS INSTITUTION. *Guide to the use of industrial by-products and waste materials in building and civil engineering,* BS 6543. BSI (London), 1987

CORBITT, R.A. *et al.* In: *Standard Handbook of Environment Engineering.* McGraw Hill (New York), 1990, pp 9-1 to 9-125

Croner's Hazardous Waste Disposal Guide. First Edition. Croner Publications Ltd (New Malden), 1988

DEPARTMENT OF THE ENVIRONMENT. *Landfill completion.* Waste Management Paper No. 26A. HMSO (London), 1992

DEPARTMENT OF THE ENVIRONMENT. *Landfill gas.* Waste Management Paper No. 27, 2nd edition. HMSO (London), 1991

DEPARTMENT OF THE ENVIRONMENT. *Landfilling wastes: A technical memorandum for the disposal of wastes on landfill sites.* Waste Management Paper No. 26. HMSO (London), 1986

DEPARTMENT OF THE ENVIRONMENT. *Licensing of waste management facilities.* Waste Management Paper No. 4. HMSO (London), 1994

DEPARTMENT OF THE ENVIRONMENT. *Special Wastes: A technical memorandum providing guidance on their definition.* Waste Management Paper No. 23 (Rev). HMSO (London), 1987

DEPARTMENT OF THE ENVIRONMENT, WELSH OFFICE. *Landfill sites: Development Control.* Joint Circular (17/89, 38/89)

DEPARTMENT OF THE ENVIRONMENT, WELSH OFFICE, SCOTTISH OFFICE. *Environmental Protection Act 1990, Waste Management, the Duty of Care, A Code of Practice.* HMSO (London), 1991

DEPARTMENT OF TRANSPORT. *Specification for Highway Works.* 7th edition. HMSO (London), 1992

GORDON, D.L. *et al.* The Stockley Park project. In: *Building on marginal and derelict land.* Thomas Telford (London), 1987, p 359-379

GUTT, W., *et al. A survey of the locations, disposal and prospective uses of the major industrial by-products and waste materials.* BRE (Watford), 1974

HEALTH AND SAFETY EXECUTIVE. *Avoiding danger from underground services.* HS (G) 47. HMSO (London), 1989

HEALTH AND SAFETY EXECUTIVE. *Entry into confined spaces.* GS 5. HMSO (London), 1977

HEALTH AND SAFETY EXECUTIVE. *Occupational exposure limits.* EH 40/94. HMSO (London), 1994

HEALTH AND SAFETY EXECUTIVE. *Protection of workers and the general public during the development of contaminated land.* HS (G) 66. HMSO (London), 1991

HORNER, P.C. *Earthworks.* ICE Works Construction Guides. Thomas Telford Ltd (London), 1981

INSTITUTION OF CIVIL ENGINEERS. *Conditions of Contract and Forms of Tender, Agreement and Bond.* 6th edition. ICE (London), 1991

INSTITUTION OF CIVIL ENGINEERS. *Specification for Ground Treatment.* ICE (London), 1987

LAWSON, E.M., *et al. A survey of the locations, disposal and prospective uses of the major industrial by-products and waste materials in Scotland.* BRE (Watford), 1978

LORD, J.A. Options available for problem solving. In: *Recycling Derelict Land,* ed. G Fleming. Thomas Telford (London), 1992, pp 145-195

PAYTON, M. Case Study: Timberyard land reclamation project in St Helens. In: *Proceedings of a Conference on Contaminated Land.* Paper No. 7. Construction Study Centre (Birmingham), September 1992

ROBINSON, P. Timberyard land reclamation scheme, St Helens. In: *Proceedings of a Conference on Contaminated Land.* Paper No 5. Construction Study Centre (Birmingham), April 1992

ROYAL COMMISSION ON ENVIRONMENT POLLUTION. *Managing Waste: The Duty of Care.* Eleventh Report. HMSO (London), 1985

RUTLAND GROUP. *Bedfont Lakes: Evolution and Progress.* Company literature, undated

SHERWOOD, P.T. *Wastes for imported fill.* Thomas Telford Ltd (London), 1987

SOMERVILLE, S.H. *Control of groundwater for temporary works.* Report 113. CIRIA (London), 1986

STEEDS, J.E. SHEPHERD, E and BARRY, D.L. *A guide to safe working practices for contaminated sites.* Report 132. CIRIA (London), 1996

The SITEFILE Digest. The Environment Press (Bath), updated quarterly

UNITED STATES ENVIRONMENTAL PROTECTION AGENCY. *Demonstration of a trial excavation at the McColl Superfund site.* Applications Analysis Report, EPA/540/AR-92/015. USEPA Office of Research and Development (Washington DC), 1992

UNITED STATES ENVIRONMENTAL PROTECTION AGENCY. *Handbook: Remediation of Contaminated Sediments.* EPA/625/6-91/28. USEPA Office of Research and Development (Washington DC), 1991

WELSH OFFICE. *An assessment of the effectiveness of the methods and systems used to reclaim contaminated sites in Wales.* Report for the Welsh Office prepared by Richards Moorehead and Laing, 1988

INDEX

Note: Numbers in italics refer to Tables. B indicates a Box, and Ap indicates an Appendix

access *see* sites, access to
accidents, planning for *44*
advisers, formalisation of relations 45
air pollution 24, *24*
ancillary measures 20-6
applicability 6-7
approvals
   legal and practical aspects *44*
   and legislation 28-31
asbestos, protective measures against 31
atmospheric emissions control, at McCoil
   Superfund site 26B

boundary definition 7-10
   investigation before excavation 9
   need of 7
   sampling during investigation 9

case study, validation, post-treatment 50B
Code of Practice for Earthworks (BS

6031) 42
contaminants
   containment and monitoring 1
   remaining as a hazard 1
   transfer 24, *24*
contaminated effluents *see* effluents
contaminated material, storage 33
contamination
   data on nature and extent 4
   hotspots 20
   planning/management responsibilities
     42
contracts *44*
contractual arrangements 44-5
Control of Substances Hazardous to
   Health (COSHH) Regulations (1988)
   23, 31
controlled waters, discharge into 31
costs
   cost breakdowns 52-3

direct *52*, 53B
excavation and off-site disposal 2
indirect *52*
operation and maintenance 52
typical 53-4
crushing plant *14*
debris, provision for *14*
dewatering sludges 13, 37-8, *38*
disposal *see* off-site disposal; on-site
   disposal
dredging equipment *36*
'Duty of Care' provisions of the
   Environmental Protection Act (1990) 1,
   13, 15, 16, 29

earthmoving operations and plant 34B
effluents, disposal of 30-1
emergency procedures 57Ap
engineering factors 10
environmental (impact) assessment (EIA)
   3, 29
environmental protection *11*
   laboratory support for monitoring 39
Environmental Protection Act (EPA)
   (1990) 1, 3, 13, 15, 16, 29, 30
equipment *see* plant and equipment
excavation
   costs 53, *54*
   integrated with other remedial
      methods 20
   limitations 9, 48, *49*
   obstructions 12-13
   partial 25
   planning *43*
   previously built on sites 12
   prognosis 55
   recycling of materials 2
   safety plans 56-7Ap
   sediments 12
   with tanks/pipework/vessels 12
   temporary measures 20B
   under enclosure 26B
excavation and off-site disposal
   advantages/disadvantages 1-2
   costs 2
excavation and on-site disposal 2-3
   flow chart for *8*
   owner responsibilities 3
excavation plant/equipment 35-6
   dredging equipment *36*, 37
   examples of *36*
   for sediments and sludges 36-7
   selection of 11-12, 36B

first aid procedures 57Ap

geotechnical properties of sites 4
ground conditions, dangers from when
   poor *22*
groundwater
   disposal/treatment of contaminated 16
   pollution of *24*
   reasons for treating 6-7
guidance applicability 5

hazardous areas, delineation of 56Ap
hazardous materials, remaining on-site
   25
hazards *see* health and safety
health and safety
   contamination problems to *22*
   dangers from plant and machinery 21
   from heavy equipment *22*
   from poor ground conditions *22*
   laboratory support for 39
   and poor safety practices 23
   and prolonged contamination contact
      problems 21
   provision of *11*
Health and Safety at Work Act (1974) 31
health surveillance 57Ap
hotspots of contamination 20
hydrological conditions 6
hydrological properties of sites 4
hygiene facilities 56Ap

in-ground barriers 20
information requirements 3-4
instruction 57Ap

laboratory support/analysis 39
legal issues, on-site disposal *17*
legislation and approvals 28-31
licensing arrangements 29-30
liquid effluents, disposal/treatment of
   contaminated 16

McCoil Superfund site, atmospheric
   emissions control at 26B
management
   excavation and disposal issues *44*
   and on-site disposal *17*
   project management *44*
   see also planning and management
Management of Health and Safety at
   Work (MHSW) regulations (1992) 23,
   31
materials handling 13-14
materials replacement 18-19
   contamination specification for 19B
   long-term considerations 19

primary/secondary sources for 19
quality assurance/quality control 19
monitoring
  for compliance, laboratory support
  for 39
  programme factors 21B
  purpose of 21

National Rivers Authority 31
noise, from heavy equipment *24*

objectives 6
  remedial 47
obstructions, excavating with 12-13
occupational health 31
off-site disposal
  costs *52, 54*
  and excavation 1-2
  key requirements 15
  limitations 48, *49*
  planning *43*
  receiving site constraints 15
  transport aspects 15
  transport methods 15
on-site disposal
  approvals for 16
  costs 52, 53B, *54*
  and excavation 2-3
  land development constraints 16
  legal issues *17*
  limitations 48, *49*
  long-term waste security
    considerations 16
  managerial issues *17*
  planning *43*
  technical issues *17*
  waste designated areas 16
operational requirements 28-40
owner of site, responsibilities 3

performance 47-50
  dependent factors 47
personal protective equipment (PPE)
  57Ap
personnel needs 39-40
planning conditions 29
planning and management
  basic issues 41-2
  contingency planning *44*
  for excavation and disposal *43*
planning permission 28-9
plant and equipment 33-8
  earthmoving operations and plant 34B
  examples to meet specific needs *34*
  heavy, health and safety aspects *22*

see also excavation plant/equipment
post-treatment
  management, laboratory support for 39
  planning *43*
preparatory works 10-11, *11*
  planning 43
procurement 45
prognosis 55
project management *44*
protective measures for operatives 23
proven applications 48, 50B
public health 2
  and environmental protection 23-5,
    26B
  laboratory support for 39

receiving site, constraints on 15
records 57Ap
recycling of excavated materials 2
refinery sludge, acidic, disposal of 26B
residues 13
risks, summary for safety plan 56Ap

safety *see* health and safety
safety and control procedures 56Ap
safety plans, for excavation 56-7Ap
scheduling *44*
security *see* site security
security, site *11*
sediments
  excavation 12
  excavation plant for 36-7
  separation equipment for 37
segregation of
  contaminated/uncontaminated materials
    13, *14*
separation
  solids/liquids 13, *14*, 37
  see also dewatering; sludges
service areas *11*
sewerage systems, discharge into 31
site characterisation data 3-4, 47
  laboratory support for 39
site condition investigation, reasons for 9
site division *11*
site monitoring 57Ap
site preparation *see* preparatory works
site requirements 32
site security 33
site services 33
site specific factors
  limitations 48, *49*
  target concentrations 50B
site supervision 56Ap
sites

access to *11*, 29, 32
  large 2-3
Sites of Special Interest (SSSIs) 10-11
sludges
  dewatering equipment/techniques 13,
    37-8, *38*
  excavation plant for 36-7
Specification for Ground Treatment (ICE:
  1987) 42
specifications, technical 42, *44*
statutory requirements 29
storage 33
  contaminated material 33
storage areas *11*
sulphur dioxide waste disposal 26B
supervision 45-6
surface water
  pollution of *24*
  reasons for treating 6

telephone links 33
timber, burning 10
toxicological hazards *22*
traffic congestion *24*
training 57Ap
transport, from sites 15
transport regulations 31

uncertainty factors 10

uncontaminated material
  removal of 10
  segregation of 13

validation, post-treatment
  at case study 50B
  investigations for 18
  with method-based specifications 18
  with performance-based specifications
    18
  post-treatment, need for 18
  supervision of 18
vapour-suppressing foam 26B
vegetation, removal of 10
vehicles, limitations on access *11*, 29
vibration, from equipment *24*
volatile organic compounds (VOCs) 26B

warranties *44*
waste disposal facilities, information
  sources *15*
waste management licences 3, 29
Waste Regulation Authority (WRA) 15,
  30
wastes, special and difficult 54
water abstraction 31
Water Resources Act (1991) 31
wheel wash facilities 29
working hour limitations 29

6 Volume VI Containment and hydraulic measures SP106

This volume describes the use of traditional civil-engineering techniques (including surface covers, in-ground barriers and hydraulic measures) to contain contaminated material, thus preventing hazardous substances coming into contact with potential targets, such as site users and occupiers, ground and surface waters, flora and fauna and building materials.

These techniques have been used extensively in the UK for the reclamation of contaminated land. Covering methods, in particular, have been used as a means of reclaiming contaminated land at relatively low cost and with minimum delay. However, all containment methods must be addressed in terms of their long-term performance, and the need for careful design, specification, implementation and monitoring.

Volume VI places particular emphasis on the design, implementation and after-care requirements associated with containment, as well as reviewing applicability, performance, limitations, practical requirements and cost characteristics.

CONTENTS

1   INTRODUCTION
    1.1   Introduction
    1.2   Physical containment methods
    1.3   Hydraulic measures
    References

2   PHYSICAL CONTAINMENT METHODS
    2.1   Concepts and classification
    2.2   Application – general issues
    2.3   Design life considerations
    2.4   Monitoring and maintenance
    2.5   Integrating technologies
    2.6   Interaction with engineering works
    References

3   COVER TECHNIQUES
    3.1   Description
    3.2   Potential applications of the method
    3.3   Research and available guidance
    3.4   Design concepts
    3.5   Cover materials
    3.6   Examples of cover designs
    3.7   Planning and management needs
    3.8   Operational requirements

3.9 Information needs
3.10 Effectiveness of the method
3.11 Limitations of the method
3.12 Costs
3.13 Prognosis
References

4 VERTICAL BARRIER SYSTEMS
4.1 Scope
4.2 Potential applications of the method
4.3 Description of the method
4.4 Planning and management
4.5 Operational requirements
4.6 Information needs
4.7 Effectiveness of the method
4.8 Limitations
4.9 Costs
4.10 Prognosis
References

5 HORIZONTAL BARRIERS AND LINERS
5.1 Introduction
5.2 Potential applications of the method
5.3 Description of the method
5.4 Planning and management needs
5.5 Operational requirements
5.6 Information needs
5.7 Effectiveness of the method
5.8 Limitations of the method
5.9 Costs
5.10 Prognosis
References

6 HYDRAULIC MEASURES
6.1 Scope and objectives
6.2 Description
6.3 Methodology
6.4 Well systems and pumping techniques
6.5 Applicability and constraints
6.6 Monitoring and maintenance
6.7 Information needs
6.8 Integration with physical methods
References

Appendix 1   Soil suction
Appendix 2   Covering materials
Appendix 3   Example of design of soil-based cover system
Appendix 4   Design guidance for hydrostatic and chemical diffusion flow through a barrier
Appendix 5   Groundwater modelling techniques

REFERENCES

ACAR, Y.B., GALE, R.J., PUTNAM, G. and HAMED, J. Electrochemical processing of soils: its potential use in environmental geotechnology and significance of pH gradients. In: *Proceedings of the 2nd International Symposium on Environmental Geotechnology, Vol 1.* (Shanghai), 1989, pp 25-38

BEAR, J., BELJIN, M. and ROSS, R. Groundwater models. In: *Water Environment and Technology*, January 1994, pp 54-58

BELL, A.L. Jet Grouting. In: *Ground Improvement*, M P Moseley (ed.). Blackie (USA), 1993

BHUIYAN, S.I. Dynamic simulation of vertical infiltration into unsaturated soils. *Water Resources Research*, 1971, 7(6), 1597-1605

BLOEMAN, G.W. Calculation of steady state capillary rise from a groundwater table and through multi-layered soils. *Zeitschr Pilanzenern* 1980, 143, 701-719

BOUWER, E. MERCER, J. KAVANAUGH, M. and DIGIANO, F. Coping with groundwater contamination, *Jnl Water Pollution Control Federation* 6(8) pp 1414-1428. 1988

BRADSHAW A.D. and CHADWICK M.J. *The restoration of land.* Blackwell Scientific Publications (Oxford), 1980

BRITISH STANDARDS INSTITUTION BS 6316 *Test Pumping Water Wells.* BSI (London), 1983

BRITISH STANDARDS INSTITUTION. BS 6031 *Earthworks.* BSI (London), 1981

BRITISH STANDARDS INSTITUTION. BS 6543 *Guide to the use of industrial by-products and waste materials in building and civil engineering.* BSI (London), 1985

BRITISH STANDARDS INSTITUTION. BS 3882 *Topsoil.* BSI (London), 1965

BUILDING RESEARCH ESTABLISHMENT. *Slurry Trench Cut-off Walls to contain contamination.* Digest 395. BRE (Garston), July 1994

CAIRNEY, T. Clean Cover Technology. In: *Contaminated Land: Policy, Regulation and Technology.* IBC Conference (London), 6/7 February 1992

CAIRNEY, T. Soil Cover Reclamations. In: *Reclaiming Contaminated Land*, T. Cairney (ed.). Blackie (Glasgow and London), 1987, pp 144-169

CAIRNEY, T. Theory and practice of soil cover system design. In *Proc 3rd Conf. Contaminated Land: policy, regulation and technology.* IBC Technical Services (London), 1992

CAIRNEY, T. (ed.). *Contaminated Land: Problems and Solutions.* Blackie Academic and Professional (Glasgow), 1993

CAIRNEY T. and SHARROCK. Clean cover technology. In: *Contaminated Land: Problems and Solutions*, T. Cairney (ed.). Blackie (Glasgow and London), 1993

CHARLES, J.A. *Building on Fill:Geotechnical Aspects.* Building Research Establishment (Garston), 1993

CHILDS, K.A. In-ground barriers and hydraulic measures. In: *Contaminated Land Reclamation and Treatment*, Smith M.A. (ed.). NATO Challenges of Modern Society Volume 8. Plenum Press (New York), 1985, pp 145-182

CHILDS, K.A. Mathematical modelling of pollutant transport by groundwater at contaminated sites. In: *Contaminated Land Reclamation and Treatment*, Smith, M.A. (ed.) NATO Challenges of Modern Society, Volume 8. Plenum Press (New York), 1985, pp 199-205

CHILDS, K.A. Treatment of contaminated groundwater. In: *Contaminated Land Reclamation and Treatment*, SMITH, M.A. (ed.) NATO Challenges of Modern Society, Volume 8. Plenum Press (New York), 1985, pp 145-182

CIRIA. *Scope for control of urban runoff.* Report 124. CIRIA (London), 1992

CIRIA. *The engineering implications of rising groundwater levels in the deep aquifer beneath London.* Special Publication 69. CIRIA (London), 1989

COPPIN, N.J. and RICHARDS, I.G. (ed.) *Use of vegetation in civil engineering.* CIRIA/Butterworths (London), 1989

D'APPOLONIA, D.J. Soil-Bentonite Slurry Trench Cutoffs. *Journal of the Geotechnical Engineering Division*, ASCE. 106(4) pp 399-417, 1980

DAY, S.R. Extraction/interception trenches by the bio-polymer slurry drainage trench technique. *Hazardous Materials Control* Vol 4 (5), pp 27-31, 1991

DECKER, J.T. Evaluating final covers for hazardous waste landfills using a rule-based knowledge system. In: *Proc 17th RREL Hazardous Waste Research Symposium: Remedial Action, Teatment and Disposal of Hazardous Waste.* EPA/600/9-91/002. USEPA (Cincinnati), 1991, pp 460-476

DEPARTMENT OF ENVIRONMENT. *Cost effective management of reclaimed derelict sites.* HMSO (London), 1989

DEPARTMENT OF ENVIRONMENT. *Evaluation of derelict land grant schemes.* HMSO (London), 1987

DEPARTMENT OF ENVIRONMENT. Private communication, 1993

DEPARTMENT OF ENVIRONMENT. *UK landfill practice.* DOE, 1993

DEPARTMENT OF ENVIRONMENT. Waste management paper 26 – *Landfilling wastes.* HMSO (London), 1986

DEPARTMENT OF ENVIRONMENT. Waste management paper 27 – *The control of landfill gas.* HMSO (London), 1991

DEPARTMENT OF THE ENVIRONMENT. ICRCL Guidance Note 59/83 *Guidance on the assessment and redevelopment of contaminated land.* DOE (London), 1987

DEPARTMENT OF THE ENVIRONMENT. *The Reclamation and Management of Metalliferous Mining Sites.* Report by Environmental Consultancy University of Sheffield and Richards Moorehead & Laing Ltd. HMSO (London), 1994

DEPARTMENT OF TRANSPORT. *Specification for Highway Works (seventh edition).* HMSO (London), 1991

DOBSON, M.C. and MOFFAT, A.J. *The Potential for Woodland Establishment on Landfill Sites.* HMSO (London), 1993

DUTTON, R.A. and BRADSHAW, A.D. *Land reclamation in cities.* HMSO (London), 1982

FLEMING, G. (ed.). *Recycling derelict land.* Thomas Telford (London), 1991

FREEZE, R.A. and CHERRY, J.A. *Groundwater.* Prentice-Hall (Englewood Cliffs, New Jersey), 1979

FRIIS MOLLER, H. and MARKUSSEN, L.M. Groundwater pollution in urban areas. In: *Conf. Proc. Groundwater Problems in Urban Areas.* ICE (London), 1993

GOLDMAN, L.J. GREENFIELD, L.I., DAMLE, A.S. and KINSBURY, G.L. *Construction and evaluation of clay liners for waste management facilities.* EPA/530/SW-86/007F. USEPA Office of Solid Waste and Emergency Response, 1988

GUTT, W., NIXON, P.J., SMITH, M.A., HARRISON, W.H. AND RUSSEL, A.D. *A survey of the locations, disposal and prospective uses of the major industrial by-products and waste materials.* Current Paper 19/74. Building Research Establishment (Garston), 1974

HALL, D.H. and MARSHALL, P. The role of construction quality assurance in the installation of geomembrane lines. In: *The Planning and Engineering of Landfills.* Midlands Geotechnical Society (Birmingham), 1992

HARVEY, S.J. Effective control of groundwater by use of ground freezing. In: *Groundwater Problems in Urban Areas.* ICE (London), 1993

HASS, H.J. and HITZE, R. *All-round encapsulation of hazardous wastes by means of injection gels and cut-off materials resistant to aggressive agents.* ESME3 Seminar on Hazardous Waste. (Bergamo, Italy), 1986

HEMPHILL, R.W. and BRAMLEY, M.E. *Protection of river and canal banks.* CIRIA/Butterworths (London), 1990

HOLDEN, J.M.W., JONES, M.A., MIRALES-WILHELM, F. and WHITE, C. *Hydraulic measures for the treatment and control of groundwater pollution.* FR/CP/26. CIRIA (London), 1995

HORNER, P.C. *Earthworks.* 2nd edition

HOUSE OF COMMONS SELECT COMMITTEE ON THE ENVIRONMENT. *First report on Contaminated Land.* HMSO (London), 1990

HOWSAM, P. (ed.) *Microbiology in Civil Engineering.* Cranfield Institute of Technology, September 1990

IBC TECHNICAL SERVICES. *Groundwater Pollution.* IBC (London), 1992

INSTITUTION OF CIVIL ENGINEERS. *Building on Marginal and Derelict Land.* Thomas Telford (London), 1987

INSTITUTION OF CIVIL ENGINEERS. *Condition and forms of tender agreement and bond for use in connection with works of civil engineering construction.* 6th edition. Thomas Telford (London), 1991

INSTITUTION OF CIVIL ENGINEERS. *New Engineering Contract.* Thomas Telford (London), 1993

INSTITUTION OF CIVIL ENGINEERS. *Specification for piling and notes for guidance.* Thomas Telford (London), 1988

INTERNATIONAL ORGANISATION FOR STANDARDISATION. *Method for determining pressure potential using a tensionmeter.* ISO/DIS 11276 (BS 7755. Part 5. Section 5.2). DIS circulated 1992

JASPERSE, B.H. AND RYAN, C.R. Stabilisation and fixation using soil mixing. *Proc. ASCE. Spec. Conf. on Grouting, Soil Improvement and Geosynthetics.* ASCE (New Orleans), 1992, pp 1273-1284

JEFFERIS, S.A. Bentonite-cement cut-off walls for waste containment: from specification to in-situ performance. *Symposium on management and control of waste fill sites.* (Leamington Spa), 1990

JEFFERIS, S.A. Contaminant grout interaction. In: *ASCE Speciality conference on grouting, soil improvement and geosynthetics.* ASCE (New Orleans), 1992

JEFFERIS, S.A. Cut-off walls: Methods, materials and specifications. In: *Proc. Int. Conf. on Construction on Polluted and Marginal Land.* Brunel University (London), 1990

JEFFERIS, S.A. In-ground barriers. In: *Contaminated Land: Problems and Solutions,* T. Cairney (ed.). Blackie (London), 1993

JEWELL, R.A. *Soil reinforcement with geotextiles.* Special Publication 123. CIRIA (London), 1996

JOHN, N.W.M. *Geotextiles.* Blackie (Glasgow), 1987

JONES, C.J.F.P. *Revised of reinforced soil applications in developed countries.* Report No. CR263. TRL, 1991

KEELY, J.F. Modeling subsurface contaminant transport and fate. In: *Transport and fate of contaminants in the subsurface.* EPA/625/4-89/019. USEPA, 1989

KNIPE, C.V., LLOYD, J.W., LERNER, D.N. and GRESWELL, R. *Rising groundwater levels in Birmingham and the engineering implications,* Special Publication 92. CIRIA (London), 1993

KRUSEMAN, G.P. and DE RIDDER, N.A. *Analysis and interpretation of pumping test data.* Int. Inst. Land Reclam. (Wagingen), 1970

LAGEMAN, R. Electro-reclamation – State of the Art. In: *Contaminated Land: Policy, Economics and Technology.* IBL (London), 1993

LEACH, B.A. and GOODGER, H.K. *Building on Derelict Land.* Special Publication 78. CIRIA (London), 1991

LLOYD, J.W. and HEATHCOTE, J.A. *Natural Inorganic Hydrochemistry in Relations to Groundwater.* Clarendon Press, (Oxford), 1985

LORD, A. Options available for problem-solving. In: *Recycling Derelict Land,* G. Fleming (ed.). Thomas Telford (London), 1991, pp 145-195

MITCHELL, J. *Groundwater in Engineering Geology.* (London), 1986

MITCHELL, J.K. Conductive phenomena: from theory to practice. 31st Rankine lecture. *Geotechnique* Vol 4 (No 3), 1991

MOSELEY, M.P. (ed.). *Ground Improvement.* Blackie (Glasgow), 1993

NATIONAL RIVERS AUTHORITY. *Policy and Practice for the Protection of Groundwater.* NRA (Bristol), 1992

NILSSON, B. and JAKOBSEN, R. *The separation pumping technique.* NATO/CCMS Pilot Study on Demonstration of remedial action technologies for contaminated land and groundwater. 4th International Conference (France), 1990

OWEIS, I.S. and KHERA, R.P. *Geotechnology of Waste Management.* Butterworth (London), 1990

PARKHURST, D.L., THORSTENSON, D.C. and PLUMMER, L.N. *PHREEQE – A computer program for geotechnical calculations.* US Geological Survey Water Resources Investigations 80-96, National Technical Information Services Report PB81-167-01 (Springfield VA), 1950

PARKINSON, C.D. The permeability of landfill liners to leachate. In: *The planning and engineering of landfills.* Midland Geotechnical Society (Birmingham), 1992

PAUL, V. *Performance of buildings materials in contaminated land.* BRE (Garston), 1994

PHILIPP HOLTZMAN AKTIENGESELLSCHAFT. *Innovative Glastechnologie für Deponiedichtwande.* 1991

PRICE, M. *Introducing Groundwater.* Chapman and Hall, 1985

PRIVETT, M.D., MATTHEWS, S.E. and HODGES, R.A. *Barriers, liners and cover systems for containment and control of land contamination.* Special Publication 124. CIRIA (London), 1996

RANKILOR, P.R. *UTF Geosynthetics Manual: A technical manual for the design of UTF geosynthetics into civil and marine engineering projects.* UCO Technical Fabrics NV (Belgium), 1992

RICHARDS MOOREHEAD & LAING LTD. *An assessment of the effectiveness of the methods and systems used to reclaim contaminated sites in Wales.* Welsh Office (Cardiff), 1988

ROLLIN, A. AND RIGO, J.M. (ed.). *Geomembranes: Identification and Performance Testing.* RILEM Report 4. Chapman and Hall (London), 1991

RUSHTON, K.R. Modelling groundwater systems. In: *Case-studies in groundwater resources evaluation.* J.W. Lloyd (ed.). Clarendon Press (Oxford), 1981

SCHROEDER, P.R., GIBSON, A.C. and SMOLEN, M.D. *The hydrologic evaluation of landfill performance (HELP) model: Vol II, Documentation for Version 1.* EPA/530-SW-84-010. USEPA (Cincinnati), 1984

SCHROEDER, P.R., MORGAN, J.M., WALSKI, T.M. and GIBSON, A.C. *The hydrologic evaluation of landfill performance (HELP) model: Vol I, User's guide for Version 1.* EPA/530-SW-84-009. USEPA (Cincinnati), 1984

SHACKLEFORD, C. D. Transit-time design of earthen barriers. *Engineering geology,* Vol 29, 1990, pp 79-94

SHARROCK T. Methods of evaluating soil cover materials and quantifying design proposals. *Civil Engineering Tech* 1986, 9 (8) 2-11

SHERWOOD, P.T. *Wastes for imported fill.* Thomas Telford (London), 1987

SIMPSON, B., BLOWER, T., CRAIG, R.N. and WILKINSON, W.B. *The engineering implications of rising groundwater levels in the deep aquifer beneath London.* Special Publication 69. CIRIA (London), 1989

SITE INVESTIGATION STEERING GROUP *Guidance Notes for the Safe Drilling of Landfills and Contaminated Land.* Site Investigation for Construction Series, Vol 4. Thomas Telford (London), 1993

SMITH, M.A. (ed.). *Contaminated land: reclamation and treatment.* NATO Challenges of Modern Society, Vol 8. Plenum Press (New York), 1985

SMITH, M.A. and BELL, R.M. Upward movement of metals into soil covering metalliferous waste. In: *Contaminated Soil,* J.W. Assink and W.J. van den Brink (eds.). Martinus Nijhaff Publishers (Dordrecht), 1985, pp 133-135

SMITH, M.A. and HARRIS, M.R. *The environmental implications of the disposal and utilisation of fly ash.* M & Q Environment, 1987 vol 1 (2), pp 10-13

SMITH, M.A. Available reclamation methods. In: *Reclaiming Contaminated Land,* T. Cairney (ed.). Blackie (Glasgow and London), 1987, pp 114-143

SMITH, M.A. Expansive slags. *Building Technical File,* 1987, No 17, pp 29-32

SOLT, G.S. and SHIRLEY, C.B. *An Engineer's Guide to Water Treatment.* Avebury Technical (Aldershot), 1991

SOMERVILLE, S.H. *Control of groundwater for temporary works.* Report 113. CIRIA (London), 1986

STEEDS, J.E., SHEPHERD, E. and BARRY, D.L. *A Guide to safe working practices for contaminated sites*, Report 132. CIRIA (London), 1996

STIEF, K. Long-term effectiveness of remedial measures. In: *Contaminated Land: Reclamation and Treatment*, M.A. Smith (ed.). Plenum (London), 1985, pp 13-36

TEDD, P., PAUL, V. and LOMAX, C. *Investigation of an eight year-old slurry trench wall*. Green '93. Bolton Institute of Higher Education (Bolton), 28 June-1 July

The Civil Engineering Standard Method of Measurement, 2nd edition. Thomas Telford (London), 1985

UNITED STATES ENVIRONMENTAL PROTECTION AGENCY. *Basics of Pump-and-Treat Ground-water Remediation Technology*. EPA/600/8-90/003. USEPA, 1990

UNITED STATES ENVIRONMENTAL PROTECTION AGENCY. *FLEX: Flexible membrane Liner Advisory expert system. Users guide*. Version 2.0. USEPA, 1987

UNITED STATES ENVIRONMENTAL PROTECTION AGENCY. *Groundwater Volume II: Methodology*. EPA/625/6-90/016b. USEPA, 1991

UNITED STATES ENVIRONMENTAL PROTECTION AGENCY. *Guidance on Remedial Actions for Contaminated Groundwater at Superfund Sites*. EPA/540/G-88/003. USEPA, 1988

UNITED STATES ENVIRONMENTAL PROTECTION AGENCY. *Guide to Technical Resources for the Design of Land Disposal Facilities*. EPA/625/6-88/018. USEPA, 1988

UNITED STATES ENVIRONMENTAL PROTECTION AGENCY. *Stabilisation technologies for RCRA Corrective actions*. EPA/625/6-91/026. August 1991

UNITED STATES ENVIRONMENTAL PROTECTION AGENCY. *Transport and fate of contaminants in the subsurface*. EPA/625/4-89/019. USEPA, 1989

US ENVIRONMENTAL PROTECTION AGENCY. *Relationship of laboratory- and field-determined hydraulic conductivity in compact clay layer*. EPA/600/2-90/025. US Environmental Protection Agency, Risk Reduction Engineering Laboratory (Cincinnati), 1990

WALTON, W.C. *Groundwater Resources Evaluation*. McGraw Hill (New York), 1970

WRIGLEY, N. Plastics in the ground – the performance of polymer materials. In: *Chemistry and Industry*, 4 July 1988, pp 414-420

INDEX

Note: Numbers in italics refer to Tables. B indicates a Box, and Ap indicates an Appendix

active containment barriers *59*, 68-9
  costs *85*
advection contaminant movement 120
advection/dispersion modelling 147ApB

aerobic (oxidising) conditions 26
approvals and consents from regulatory
  bodies 79
aquifer properties/tests 119, *123*

barriers *see* horizontal barriers; vertical
  barriers
basal liners 91, 96
batch flushing, modelling 146ApB
Bedfont Lakes excavated barriers 65B
bentonite clay slurry 72
bentonite-cement slurry 72
bio-barrier barrier technique *59, 66*
  costs *85*
boring, for data collection *123*
break-through time 76
bucket and grab-type machines *82*
Building Research Establishment 9
butyl rubber 132Ap

capillary forces 25
capping, slurry walls 85-6
capping layers 6
cellular concrete 130Ap
chemical attack on cover materials 33B
chemical diffusion flow through a barrier
  138-40Ap
chemical migration 76
claquage grouting 92-3
clay barriers
  advantages/disadvantages *64*
  compacted clay 64
  cracking 51
  desiccation of clayey covers 33B
  estuarine clay, physical properties *24*
clay-cement cut-off barrier material *71,*
  72
clay-cement-aggregate cut-off barrier
  material *71*, 72
clay-cement-aggregate cut-off with
  membranes barrier material *71*, 73-4
commercial land use, and cover systems
  design *31*
compacted clay barriers 64
conductivity, and suction 24
cones of depression 108-9
consents and approvals from regulatory
  bodies 79
containment
  integration with hydraulic methods
    123
  see also cover methods/techniques;
    horizontal barriers and liners;
    hydraulic measures; physical
    containment; vertical barriers
contaminant information needs 119-23
contaminant movement/migration
  by advection 120
  pathways downward 24-5
  pathways upward 21-4, *23*

soil characteristic effects 25-7
water soluble 22
see also groundwater
  models/modelling
contaminants
  characterisation of 121
  concentrations and areal extent *122*
  priority 120
  types of material 17-18
contamination hot spots 18
continuous flushing modelling 147ApB,
  148ApB
contracts, conditions of 79
contractual arrangements 48
costs
  estimation of 52-3
  horizontal barriers 97
  and risks 10
  vertical barrier techniques 85-6, 85B
cover materials 34-9
  modified soils 35, 130Ap
  natural *35*
  soil based 41-4, 129-30Ap, 135-7Ap
  synthetic *35*, 44-6, 130-3Ap
  waste material *35*
cover methods/techniques
  application modes 18-19
  contaminant movement 21-7
  costs 52-3
  design examples 39-44
  design life 11-12, 29-30
  design requirements/objectives *20*, 21
  failure mechanisms 33-4
  functions 17
  information needs 49
  limitations 16-17, 51-2
  method effectiveness 49-50
  operational requirements 49
  pathway control 27-9
  planning 47
  porous pavements *131*Ap
  principle 6, 16
  reinforcement *131*Ap
  research and available guidance 19-21
  and site end use 30-2
  specifications 47-8
cyanide 26
cyclic pumping 115

data collection methods *123*
dense non-aqueous phase liquids
  (DNAPLs) 121
Department of the Environment (DoE)
  19, 52, 53
design life of systems 11-12, 29-30

discharge zone management 100
displacement barriers 59-61, *59*
   costs *85*
   principle 6
distribution coefficient 121
drainage ditches 74
drainage nets *133*Ap
drainage trenches, and hydraulic
  measures 107-8
drainage walls 74
drought
   design drought 29
   and design life 30

ecologically valuable land, and cover
  systems *32*
electrical migration 76
electro-kinetic barrier technique *59*, 66,
  70
   applications 67B, *68*, *69*
   costs *85*
electronic piezometers 110
engineering issues 13-14, *14*
Environment, Department of (DoE) 19
  and costs 52, 53
excavated barriers 6, *59*, 61-4, 65B
   costs *85*
excavation, integration with hydraulic
  methods 123

failure mechanisms
   plant/tree roots 34
   soil based systems 33B
   synthetic materials 33B
field capacity 24
Flexible Membrane Liner Advisory
  Expert System (FLEX) 132Ap
forestry land, on cover systems *32*

gas venting 18, 52
geological information needs 118
geomembranes 130-2Ap
geophysics data *123*
grass cultivators (varieties) 19
grasscrete 130Ap
'graves latier' modified soil 130Ap
ground freezing barrier technique *59*, 65
   costs *85*
groundwater
   flooding of 22
   level control and cover systems *32*
   management techniques 116
   sampling *123*
   treatment of contaminated 104
groundwater hydrology

groundwater models/modelling
   applications 143-5Ap
   contaminant behaviour 142-3Ap,
    142ApB
   groundwater flow 142-3Ap, 142ApB
   information needs 145-7Ap
   limitations 148-9Ap
   principles 140-1Ap
   remediation period prediction 146-
    8ApB
   selection of models 149Ap
   US Environmental Protection Agency
    recommendations 144Ap
grouting/ground injection
   horizontal barriers 92, *93*
   vertical barriers *59*, 64
guard ring concept 68

hard surfaced covers 46
health and safety
   artificial barriers 94
   with drainage trenches 108
   planning 47
Henry's Law Constant 120
Hereford and Worcestershire excavated
  barriers 65B
high density polyethylene (HDPE)
   membrane material 73, 132Ap
   costs of *86*
   for monitoring equipment 114
holding tanks 115
horizontal barriers and liners
   applications 90-1
   artificial, design of 93-4
   contaminant movement types 91
   costs 97
   effectiveness 96
   and high water pressures 90
   information needs 95
   limitations 96-7
   liner types 93
   naturally occurring 92
   operational requirements 95
   planning and management 94-5
   principle 8-9, *8*
   prognosis 97
   types of 91-4
hot spots, contamination 18
hydraulic conductivity 22B, *122*
hydraulic measures 3-4
   abstraction wells 106
   applications 99-106
   constraints to 122
   containment, integration with 123-5
   data collection methods *123*

drainage trenches 107-8
excavation, integration with 123
general limitations 117B
information needs 118-23
injection/infiltration wells 106
monitoring and maintenance 116-18
planning and management 114-15
plume containment 101-3
separation 100-1, *101*
for treatment purposes 103-5
upward gradients 106, *106*
see also well systems and pumping
hydraulic piezometers 110
hydrodynamic dispersion 120
hydrofacturing techniques for horizontal
barriers 92-3
*Hydrologic Evaluation for Landfill
Performance* (US EPA) 29B
hydrostatic flow of contaminants 76, 138-
40Ap

ICRCL criteria/threshold trigger levels
34-5
immiscible fluids 121B
industrial land use, and cover systems *31*
infiltration/infiltration capacity 24
effect of vegetation 25
factors governing *26*
information needs 49
injection barriers 6, *59*, 64-5
costs *85*
integrating technologies 13
intrinsic permeability 121B
ion exchange capacity 77

jet grouting *59*, 62, 65

lime, added to soil 26
liner types 93
local effective stress, on barriers 78
low density polyethylene (LDPE)
membrane material 73

maintenance, with monitoring 13
mathematical models *see* models
membrane wall barriers *59*, 61
membranes
bentonite based 133
for capping landfill sites 46
flexible 45B, 130-3Ap
low density polyethylene (LDPE) 73
low-permeability 18
polyvinyl chloride (PVC) 73, 132Ap
and slurry trench barriers 73-4
for slurry trench cut-offs 73-4

metalliferous waste sites, cover for *38*
migration *see* contaminant
movement/migration; pathways for
contaminants
models/modelling
Bhuiyan's 28
Bloemen's 28, 135-6Ap
techniques for 78
US EPA 29B
see also groundwater
models/modelling
molecular diffusion 120
monitoring
environmental *12*
HDPE, use of in equipment 114
hydraulic systems 116-18
and maintenance 13
performance *12*
planning long term 80
purposes of 12-13
and regulatory authorities 13
well systems and pumping 110

neoprene 132Ap
non-aqueous phase liquids (NAPLs) 103,
105
data on 121

octanol-water partition coefficient 120
operational requirements 49
organic carbon partition coefficient 121
organic matter, solid 26
organic vapours 18
osmotic flow of water 76

panel wall barriers 60
pathways for contaminants
control of 27-9
downward 24-5, *28*
in soiled based systems 28
upward 21-7, *27-8*
percussive tools *82*
permeability, effect of vegetation 25
permeability of barrier material 76-7
permeation grouting of horizontal
barriers 92
physical containment
applicability 9-10
concepts and classification 5-9, *7*
constraints 9-10
design life 11-12
effectiveness 10-11
integrating technologies 13
interaction with engineering works 13-
14

methods/techniques 1-2
piezometers,
 pneumatic/electronic/hydraulic 110
planning, cover systems 47
plume containment, by hydraulic means
 101-3, *102, 103*
pneumatic piezometers 110
polymer slurry 72
polymeric based sheet materials *45*, 130-
 2Ap
polymeric materials 36
polyvinyl chloride (PVC) membrane
 material 73, 132Ap
porous pavements *131*Ap
The Potential for Woodland
 Establishment on Landfill sites (DoE)
 21
procurement aspects 48
pumped sumps 111
pumped wells 111
pumping systems for treatment purposes
 104-5
 data requirements for *122*
 monitoring 110
pumping for well systems *see* well
 systems and pumping

quality control, cover systems 48

recreational land use, and cover systems
 31
regulatory authorities, and monitoring 13
relative permeability of barrier materials
 77
research and guidance in UK 19
residential land use, and cover systems *31*
residual saturation of contaminants 121B
reverse-circulation machines *82*
roots, as a cause of cover failure 33B
rotary cutting equipment 82

sand
 coarse gravelly, physical properties *24*
 fine beach, physical properties *24*
secant piling barriers *59*, 61
seepage barriers 64
self healing of barriers 78
separation, by hydraulic means 100-1,
 101
services, buried in cover materials 30
sewage systems, buried in cover materials
 30
shallow cut-off wall barriers *59*, 62
siltation of pore voids 33B
site end use 30-2

site hydrology 108
slags, unstable 33B
slurry trench barriers *59*, 63
 capping 85-6
 construction techniques 70-4, *71*
 costs *86*
 excavation equipment for *82*
 with membranes 73-4
 planning and management 80-3
soil, drilling contaminated 114
soil characteristics, and contaminant
 movement 25-7
soil chemical/physical properties, and
 well systems 109
soil mixing, horizontal barriers 92
soil moisture movement *see* pathways for
 contaminants
soil permeability 108
soil sampling *123*
soil suction 127Ap
soil water potential 127Ap
soil-active clay cut-offs 74
soil-bentonite backfills 74
soiled based systems
 design examples 41-4, *42*, *44*, 135-
 7Ap
 design stages *43*
 see also pathways for contaminants
solute transport data 120-1
sorption/sorptive properties, barriers 77,
 120
specifications
 cover systems 47-8
 technical 79
steel sheet piling barriers 59, *59*
suction and conductivity 24
suction wells 111
supervision, cover systems 48
synthetic materials
 for cover *35*, 36, 73, 114, 130-2Ap
 failure of 33B
 systems employing 44-6
technical specifications 79
thermal flow of water 76
trench excavators *82*

US Environmental Protection Agency
 (USEPA) 26B, 132Ap, 144Ap

vacuum injector wells 111, 114
vegetation, effect on permeability and
 infiltration 25
venting *see* gas venting
vertical barriers
 application mode 58

construction methods *71*
costs 85-6, *85, 86*
design requirements 75-8
displacement types 59-61, *59*
excavated types *59*, 61-4
function 57-8
information needs 83, 83B
injected types *59*, 64-5
limitations 84-5
long-term performance 86-7
method effectiveness 84
miscellaneous types *59*, 65-70
operational requirements 83
planning and management 79-83
principle 6, *8*
properties 76-8
slurry trench construction techniques
    70-4
vibrated beam wall barriers 59-60, *59*
viscous materials 18
volatile compounds 109

washboring 114
waste disposal land, cover systems for *32*
Waste Management Papers 26 and 27
    (DoE) 76
waste materials
    cover for *35*
    cover material suitability *37*

Water Resources Act (1991) 114
well systems and pumping
    abstraction wells 111-12
    acidic water, attack from 112
    bio-fouling, attack from 113
    contaminant properties, designing for
        109
    cyclic pumping 115
    injection wells 113
    installing systems 114
    metallic concentrations, attack from
        112
    monitoring wells 110
    nutrients, attack from 112
    operational requirements assessment
        110
    oxidising agents, attack from 112
    pumping 106-7
    servicing and maintenance 115-16
    siting 105
    soil chemical/physical properties 109
    solvents, attack from 112
    system design 108-11
    vacuum injector wells 114
    and volatile compounds 109
Welwyn Garden City excavated barriers
    65B
wool fibre blanket cover material 130Ap

7   Volume VII Ex-situ remedial methods for soils, sludges and sediments SP107

Volume VII describes the main process-based generic options for the ex-situ treatment of contaminated solids and semi-solids. Methods covered include thermal, physical, chemical, biological and stabilisation/solidification types. The specific materials handling requirements of the methods (before, during and after treatment) are reviewed, and plant and equipment needs, process control and on-going process monitoring requirements are highlighted.

Individual methods are reviewed in terms of their applicability, effectiveness, limitations, practical requirements and costs.

CONTENTS

1 INTRODUCTION
- 1.1   Scope
- 1.2   Selection of method
- 1.3   Applicability
- 1.4   Effectiveness
- 1.5   Materials handling and pretreatment
- 1.6   Other considerations
- 1.7   Compliance and performance testing and monitoring
- 1.8   Integration and treatment trains
- References

2 THERMAL METHODS
- 2.1   Introduction
- 2.2   Applicability
- 2.3   The main process variations
- 2.4   Operational requirements
- 2.5   Information requirements
- 2.6   Effectiveness
- 2.7   Limitations
- 2.8   Costs
- 2.9   Prognosis
- References

3 PHYSICAL METHODS
- 3.1   Introduction
- 3.2   Soil washing systems
- 3.3   Solvent extraction
- 3.4   Electro-remediation
- References

4 CHEMICAL TREATMENT METHODS

4.1 Introduction
4.2 Applicability
4.3 Principal processes
4.4 Operational requirements
4.5 Information requirements
4.6 Effectiveness
4.7 Limitations
4.8 Costs
4.9 Prognosis
References

5 BIOLOGICAL METHODS

5.1 Introduction
5.2 Applicability
5.3 Main process variations
5.4 Operational requirements
5.5 Information requirements
5.6 Effectiveness
5.7 Limitations
5.8 Costs
5.9 Prognosis
References

6 STABILISATION AND SOLIDIFICATION

6.1 Introduction
6.2 Applicability
6.3 The main process variations
6.4 Operational requirements
6.5 Information requirements
6.6 Effectiveness
6.7 Limitations
6.8 Costs
6.9 Prognosis
References

Appendix 1 Examples of elements and compounds belonging to different contaminant groups
Appendix 2 The APEG and Base Catalysed Decomposition processes
Appendix 3 The X*TRAX™ Thermal Desorption System
Appendix 4 Applicability of stabilisation/solidification methods
Appendix 5 Evaluation of performance of stabilisation/ solidification processes

REFERENCES

ANDERSON, W.C. *Innovative remediation technology: solvent/chemical extraction.* American Academy of Environmental Engineers (Annapolis), 1994

ANDERSON, W.C. (ed.) *Innovative site remediation technology: bioremediation.* American Society of Environmental Engineers (Annapolis), 1994

ANDERSON W.C. (ed.) *Innovative site remediation technology: chemical treatment.* American Academy of Environmental Engineers (Annapolis), 1994

ANDERSON, W.C. (ed.) *Monograph on innovative remediation technology: thermal desorption.* American Academy of Environmental Engineers (Annapolis), 1993

ANDERSON, W.C. (ed.) *Monograph on innovative remediation technology: thermal destruction.* American Academy of Environmental Engineers (Annapolis), 1994

ANDERSON, W.C. (ed.) *Monographs on innovative site remediation technologies.* American Academy of Environmental Engineers (Annapolis), various volumes, 1993-1995

ANDERSON, W.C. (ed.) *Soil washing/soil flushing (Monograph on Innovative Site Remediation Technology).* American Academy of Environmental Engineers (Annapolis), 1993

ANDERSON, W.C. (ed.) *Stabilisation/solidification.* American Academy of Environmental Engineers (Annapolis), 1994

ANDERSON, T.A. *et al.* Bioremediation in the rhizosphere: plant roots and associated microbes clean contaminated soil. *Environmental Science and Technology,* 1993, **27** (13), 2630-2636

ANON. AOSTRA-Taciuk Processor Performing Soil Cleanup. *The TARpaper,* 1990, **13**, 4

ANON. *Recycling waste streams using glass-making additives.* VERT Publication, October 1990

ANON. Thermal desorption system treats wide variety of solid wastes. *Tech Trends.* 1993 (May), 1-2. EPA/540/N-93/005. US Environmental Protection Agency (Washington DC)

ARMISHAW, R. *et al. Review of Innovative Contaminated Soil Clean-up Processes.* Warren Springs Laboratory (Stevenage), 1992

BARR, D.P. and AUST, S.D. Mechanisms white rot fungi use to degrade pollutants. *Environmental Science and Technology,* 1994, **28** (2) 78A-87A

BARTH, E.F. and McCANDLES, R.M. *Treatability Assessment Planning Guide for Solidification/stabilization of Contaminated Soils.* US Environmental Protection Agency (Cincinnati), 1989

BISHOP, P.L. Stabilisation/solidification of contaminated soils: An overview. In: *Proceedings of the Third International KfK/TNO Conference on Contaminated Soil '90,* Arendt, F., Hinsenveld, M. and van den Brink, W.J. (eds.) Kluwer (Dordrecht), 1990, pp 1265-1274

BOELSING, F. *Remediation of toxic waste sites: DCR technology in the field of immobilization and fixation of hazardous compounds.* Report prepared for Ministry of Economics, Technology and Traffic (Hannover), 1988

BÖHM, K. A thermal method for treating contaminated soil. In: *Contaminated land treatment technologies,* Rees, J.F. (ed.). Elsevier Applied Science (London), 1992, pp 195-219

BRIERLY, K.W. The British Nuclear Fuels 'Cacitox' soil treatment process. In: *Proceedings of the NATO/CCMS Pilot Study Meeting on Demonstration of Remedial Action Technologies for Contaminated Land and Groundwater.* (Budapest), 1992

BULLOGH, G. UK first for thermal soil remediation technique. *Industrial Waste Management,* 1994 (Sept), 26-27

CAIRNEY, T. (ed.) *Contaminated Land: Problems and Solutions.* Blackie (Glasgow), 1993

CAMPBELL, K. and McEWEN,C., SITE program demonstration of the ECO-LOGIC process on PCB-contaminated waste. In: *Proceedings of the third Annual Symposium on Groundwater and Soil Remediation.* Environment Canada (Ottawa), 1993, pp 483-495

CRAIG, H. The compositing alternative to incineration of explosives contaminated soil. USEPA *Tech. Trends* 1994 (November), 1 and 4

CUDAHY, J.J. and TROXLER, W.L. 1990 thermal remediation industry contractor survey. *J. Air and Waste Management Association,* 1991, 40, 8

CUDAHY, J.J. and TROXLER, W.L. 1991 thermal remediation industry survey. *J. Air and Waste Management Association,* 1992, 42, 844

CZARNECKI, R.C. Hot mix asphalt technology and the cleaning of contaminated soil. In: *Petroleum Contaminated Soils, Volume 1.* Calabrese, E.J. and Kostecki, P.T. (eds.) Lewis Publishers (Chelsea, Michigan), 1989, pp 267-278

DEPARTMENT OF THE ENVIRONMENT/SCOTTISH OFFICE. *UK action plan for the phasing out and destruction of polychlorinated biphenyls (PCBs) and dangerous PCB substitutes: a consultation paper.* Department of the Environment (London), 1993

DEPARTMENT OF THE ENVIRONMENT. *Waste Management Paper No. 6. Polychlorinated Biphenyls.* HMSO (London), 1994

EKLUND, K. Incorporation of contaminated soils in bituminous concrete. In: *Petroleum Contaminated Soils, Volume 1,* Calabrese, E.J. and Kostecki, P.T. (eds.). Lewis Publishers (Chelsea, Michigan), 1989, pp 190-200

EMERY, J.J. Stabilisation of industrial sludge for fill applications. In: *Volume 4, Proceedings Seventh International Congress on the Chemistry of Cement.* Paris, 1980

ENDS. *New process may offer clean-up solution for acid tar dumps.* Report No. 200. Environmental Data Services (London), September 1991

ENDS. *Soil clean-up plant clears licensing, planning hurdles.* Report No. 211. Environmental Data Services (London), August 1992, p 10

ENVIRONMENT CANADA *Proceedings of the Third Annual Symposium on Groundwater and Soil Remediation, Québec, 1993.* Ottawa, 1993

FLEMING G. (ed.). *Recycling Derelict Land.* Thomas Telford (London), 1991

GOETZ, D., HOLZ, C. and MEYENBURG, G. Change of soil properties caused by thermal treatment in a rotary kiln at 1000°C. In: *Proceedings of the Fourth*

International KfK/TNO Conference on Contaminated Soil '93. Arendt F. *et al* (eds.) Kluwer Academic Publishers (Dordrecht), 1993, pp 881-890

GUROL, M.D. and RAVIKUMAR, J.X. Chemical oxidation of hazardous compounds in soil. In: *Proceedings of the National Research and Development Conference on the Control of Hazardous Materials.* Hazardous Materials Control Research Institute (Greenbelt, Maryland), 1991, pp 296-302

GUTT, W. and SMITH, M.A. *Studies of phosphatic cements.* Building Research Establishment Current Paper CP 95/74. BRE (Garston), 1974

HARDEN, J.M. and RAMSAY, G.C. *Catalytic Dehydrohalogenation: A Chemical Destruction Method for Halogenated Organics.* EPA/600/2-86/113. US Environmental Protection Agency (Cincinnati), 1986

HEIMHARD, H.J. High-pressure soil washing. In: *Proceedings of the Second KfK/TNO Conference on Contaminated Soil '88.* Kluwer Academic Publishers (Dordrecht), 1988, pp 871-882

HELLER, H. *Poultice Method for Extracting Hazardous Spills.* US Patent 4483716, 1984

HENKE, G.A. Experience reports about on-site bioremediation of oil polluted soils. In: *Recycling International (Volume 3),* K.J. Thomé-Kozmiensky (ed.). EF-Verlag für Energie und Umwelttechnik (Berlin), 1989, pp 2178-2183

HENNIG, R. Physico-chemical soil purification with the Harbauer Process. In: *Proceedings of the Third International KfK/TNO Conference Contaminated Soil '90.* Kluwer (Dordrecht), 1990, pp 933-934

HENNING, R. Cleaning of mercury contaminated soil by using a combined washing and distillation process. In: *Proceedings of the Fourth International KfK/TNO Conference on Contaminated Soil '93,* Arendt, F. *et al* (eds.). Kluwer (Dordrecht), 1993, pp 1305-1314

HINSENVELD, M. Innovatory techniques for treatment of contaminated soils and sediments. In: *Proceedings of an International Conference on Northern Seas Environmental Challenges and Business Opportunities.* Section 3.9. (Stavanger, Norway), 1991,

HINSENVELD, M. Leaching and volatilisation from cement stabilized wastes. In: *Proceedings of the Fourth International KfK/TNO Conference on Contaminated Soil.* Kluwer (Dordecht), 1993

HINSENVELD, M.A. Sound and practical method to determine the quality of stabilization. In: *Proceedings of the First International NATO/CCMS Conference on the Evaluation of Demonstrated and Emerging Technologies for the Treatment and Cleanup of Contaminated Land and Groundwater (Phase II), (Budapest).* USEPA Risk Reduction Engineering Laboratory (Cincinnati), 1992

HINSENVELD, M.A. Sound and practical method to determine the quality of stabilization. In: *Proceedings of the Fourth International KfK/TNO Conference on Contaminated Soil,* Arendt, F. *et al* (eds.). Kluwer (Dordrecht), 1993, p 1519

HINSENVELD, M. Stabilisation/solidification Technologies. In: *Final Report of NATO/CCMS Pilot Study on Demonstration of Remedial Action Technologies for Contaminated Land and Groundwater*. EPA/600/R-93/012a. US Environmental Protection Agency (Cincinnati), 1993, pp 23-32

HOLROYD, M.L. and CAUNT, P. Fungal processing: a second generation biological treatment for the degradation of recalcitrant organics in soil. *Land Contamination and Reclamation*, 1994, **2** (4), 183-188

HUTTON, J.H. and SHANKS, R. Thermal desorption of PCB-contaminated waste at the Waukegan Harbour Superfund site. In: *Proceedings of the US Environmental Protection Agency Fourth Forum on Innovative Hazardous Waste Treatment Technologies: Domestic and International*. (San Francisco), 1992

HUTTON, J.H. Thermal desorption of PCB-contaminated waste at the Waukegan Harbor Superfund site. In: *Proceedings of the US Environmental Protection Agency, Fourth Forum on Innovative Hazardous Waste Treatment Technologies: Domestic and International*. (San Francisco), 1992

IKEGUCHI, T. and GOTOH, S. Thermal treatment of contaminated soil with mercury. In: *Final Report NATO/CCMS Pilot Study: Demonstration of remedial Action Technologies for Contaminated Land and Groundwater, Volume 2 – Part 2*. US Environmental Protection Agency (Cincinnati), 1993, pp 974-985

JAMES, S.C. and STACY, G.L., Thermal technologies. In: *Final Report NATO/CCMS Pilot study on Demonstration of Remedial Action technologies for Contaminated Land and Groundwater, Volume 1*. EPA/600/R-93/012a. US Environmental Protection Agency (Cincinnati), 1993, pp 7-22

KORNEL, A. and ROGERS, C. PCB Destruction: A Novel Dehalogenation Reagent *Journal of Hazardous Materials*, 1985, 12, 161-176

KOSTECKI, P.T., CALABRESE, E.J. and FLEISCHER, E.J. Asphalt batching of petroleum contaminated soils. In: *Petroleum Contaminated Soils, Volume 1*, Calabrese, E.J. and Kostecki, P.T. (eds.). Lewis Publishers (Chelsea, Michigan), 1989, pp 175-190

LAGEMAN, R. Electro-reclamation: State of the art. In: *Proceedings of a Conference on Contaminated Land Policy, Economics and Technology*. Paper No. 9. IBC Technical Services (London), 1993

LAPINSKAS, J. Bacterial biodegradation of petroleum hydrocarbons: An alternative technology for soil and groundwater decontamination. In: *Proceedings of a Conference on Contaminated Land Policy, Regulation and Technology*. Paper No. 8. IBC (London), 1990

LAPINSKAS, J. Bacterial degradation of hydrocarbon contamination in soil and groundwater. *Chemistry and Industry*, December 1989, pp 784-789

LEA, F.M. *Chemistry of Cement and Concrete*. Edward Arnold (London), 1970

LEACH, B.A. and GOODGER, H.K. *Building on Derelict Land*. Special Publication 78. CIRIA (London), 1991

MacKAY, M. and EMERY, J.J., Practical stabilisation of contaminated soils. *Land contamination and reclamation*, 1993, 1 (3), 144-145

MACKENBROCK, K. *et al.* Industrial scale testing of DBA pyrolysis process for treatment of organically contaminated soils. In: *Proceedings of the Third International KfK/TNO Conference on Contaminated Soil '90.* Kluwer (Dordrecht), 1990, 905-906

MAJOR, M.A. and AMOS, J.C. Incineration of explosive-contaminated soil. *Hazardous Materials Control*, 1993, **6** (1), 26-27

McNEILL, K.R. and WARING. S. Vitrification of contaminated soil. In: Rees, J.F. (ed.), *Contaminated land treatment technologies.* Elsevier Applied Science (London), 1992, pp 143-159

McNEILL, K.R. Vitrification: a simple technology for recycling large quantities of industrial waste and contaminated soil. In: *Proceedings of a Conference on Contaminated Land: Policy Economics and Technology.* IBC Technical Services (London), 1993

NADEN, D. In-pulp decontamination of contaminated soils/sludges/sediments and residues. In: *Proceedings of a Conference on Contaminated Land: Policy, Economics and Technology.* IBC Technical Services (London), 1993

OLFENBUTTEL, R. The application of an innovative base-catalysed decomposition process to PCB contaminated soils. In: *Proceedings of a Conference on Contaminated Land: Policy, Economics and Technology.* IBC Technical Services (London), 1993

OWEN, F. and MAIDMENT, D. (eds.). *Quality assurance: a guide to the application of ISO 9001 to process plant projects.* Institution of Chemical Engineers (Rugby), 1993

PETERSON, R.L. APEG-Plus™: Dechlorination of Soils and Sludges. In: *Proceedings of a Symposium on Hazardous Waste Treatment: Treatment of Contaminated Soils.* Air & Waste Management Association (Pittsburgh), 1990, pp 94-99

PETERSON, R.L. *Method for Decontaminating Soil.* US Patent 4574013, 1986

PETERSON, R.L. *Method for Reducing Content of Halogenated Aromatics in Hydrocarbon Solutions.* US Patent 4530228, 1985

PETERSON, R.L. *Methods for Decontaminating Soil.* US Patent 4447541, 1984

PORTLAND CEMENT ASSOCIATION. *Solidification and stabilization of wastes using Portland cement.* PCA (Skokie IL), 1991

PYTLEWSKI, L.L. and KREVITZ, K. *Method for Decomposition of Halogenated Organic Compounds.* US Patent 4400552, 1983

RENOUX, A.Y., ROY, Y., TYAGI, R.D. and SAMSOM, R. Ecotoxicological evaluation of soil biotreatment: comparison with the inherent toxicity of non-contaminated soils. In: *Proceedings of the Third Annual Symposium on Groundwater and Soil Remediation, Québec, 1993.* Environment Canada (Ottawa), 1993

RENTJES, R.C. and SCHULER, C. Ten years experience in thermal soil treatment. In: *Proceedings of the Third International KfK/TNO Conference on Contaminated Soil '90.* Kluwer (Dordrecht), 1990, pp 885-893

ROGERS, C., KORNEL, A. and SPARKS, H. *Method for the Destruction of Halogenated Organic Compounds in a Contaminated Medium.* US Patents 5019175 (28 May 1991) and 5039350 (13 August 1991)

ROGERS, C.J. and KORNEL, A. *Chemical Destruction of Halogenated Aliphatic Hydrocarbons.* US Patent 4675464, 1987

ROGERS, C.J., KORNEL, A. and SPARKS, H.L. *Base Catalyzed Decomposition of Toxic and Hazardous Chemicals.* US Environmental Protection Agency (Cincinnati), 1991

RULKENS, W.H. *et al.* On-site processing of contaminated soil. In: *Contaminated Land: Reclamation and Treatment*, M.A. Smith (ed.). Plenum Press (New York), 1985, pp 37-90

SIMS, J.C., *et al. Bioremediation of contaminated surface soils.* EPA/600/9-89/073. USEPA Robert S. Kerr Environmental Research Laboratory (Ada OK), 1989

SMITH, J.D., Treatment council calls 'foul' on desorbers. *Environmental Information Digest*, 1993 (August), 23-24

SMITH, M.A. (ed.) *Contaminated Land: Reclamation and Treatment.* Plenum Press (New York), 1985

SMITH, M.A. and HARRIS, M.R. The environmental implications of the disposal and utilisation of fly ash. *M & Q Environment*, 1987, 1, (2), 10-13

SMITH, M.A. and OSBORNE, G.J. Slag/fly ash cements. *World Cement Technology*, 1977, 8, (6), 223-233

SOCZO, E.R., *et al.* Ten years of soil clean-up in the Netherlands (Dutch contribution to the Round Table Discussion on National Programmes). In: *Proceedings of the First Meeting of Phase II of the NATO/CCMS Pilot Study on Evaluation of Demonstrated and Emerging Technologies for the Treatment of Contaminated Land and Groundwater.* (Budapest), 1990

SOUNDARAJAN, R. Organic stabilization/solidification: theory and practice. In: *Contaminated Land Treatment Technologies*, Rees, J.F. (ed.). Elsevier Applied Science (Barking), 1992, pp 160-179

SPOONER, P.E., *et al. Compatibility of grouts with hazardous wastes.* EPA/600-2-84-015. US Environmental Protection Agency (Cincinnati), 1984

STAPS, S. Microbial Treatment Technologies. In: *Final Report of the NATO/CCMS Study on Demonstration of Remedial Action Technologies for Contaminated Land and Groundwater.* EPA/600/R-93/012a. US Environmental Protection Agency (Cincinnati), 1993, pp 85-107

STEGEMANN, J.A. and COTE, P.L. *Investigation of test methods for solidified waste evaluation – A cooperative program.* Report EPS 3/HA/8, Environment Canada (Ottawa), 1991

TACIUK, W. and RITCEY, R.M. PCB decontamination of soils and sludges with the AOSTRA Taciuk process. In: *Proceedings of Haztech Canada: Fourth Annual Environmental Conference.* (Calgary), 1991

TACIUK, W., Thermal processes – recovery of hydrocarbons through anaerobic pyrolysis using the AOSTRA-Taciuk processor. In: *Proceedings of the Second Annual Conference on Cleanup of Contaminated Sites.* (Toronto), 1992

TAYLOR, H.F.W. *Cement Chemistry.* Academic Press (London), 1990

TROXLER, W.L., CUDAHY, R.P., ROSENTHAL, S.I. and YEZZI, J.J. Treatment of petroleum contaminated soils by thermal desorption technologies. In: *Proceedings of 85th Annual Meeting, Air and Waste Management Association.* (Kansas City), 1992

US ENVIRONMENTAL PROTECTION AGENCY. *Acid extraction treatment systems for treatment of metal-contaminated soils.* Emergency Technology Summary. USEPA (Cincinnati), 1994

US ENVIRONMENTAL PROTECTION AGENCY. *AOSTRA-Soiltech anaerobic thermal processor: Wide Beach development site.* Demonstration Bulletin. USEPA (Cincinnati), 1992

US ENVIRONMENTAL PROTECTION AGENCY. *AOSTRA-SoilTech Anaerobic Thermal Processor Treats PCBs in Soils at Wide Beach Development Superfund site in Brant, New York.* USEPA (Cincinnati), 1991

US ENVIRONMENTAL PROTECTION AGENCY. Babcock & Wilcox Co. (Cyclone furnace). In: *The Superfund Innovative Technology Evaluation Program: Technology Profiles.* 6th edition, EPA/540/R-93/526. USEPA Office of Solid Waste and Emergency Response (Washington DC), 1993, pp 24-25

US ENVIRONMENTAL PROTECTION AGENCY. *Babcock and Wilcox Cyclone Furnace Vitrification Technology.* Applications Analysis Report, EPA/540/AR-92/017. USEPA Risk Reduction Engineering Laboratory Office of Research and Development (Cincinnati), 1992

US ENVIRONMENTAL PROTECTION AGENCY. *BCD: An EPA-Patented Process for Detoxifying Chlorinated Wastes.* USEPA (Cincinnati)

US ENVIRONMENTAL PROTECTION AGENCY. *Biogenesis™ soil washing technology.* Application Analysis Report, EPA/540/R-93/510. USEPA Office of Research and Development (Washington DC), 1993

US ENVIRONMENTAL PROTECTION AGENCY. Biotrol, Inc (Soil washing system). In: *The Superfund Innovative Technology Evaluation Program: Technology Profiles.* 6th edition, EPA/540/R-93/526), pp 34-35. USEPA Office of Research and Development (Washington DC), 1993

US ENVIRONMENTAL PROTECTION AGENCY. *BioTrol Soil Washing System for Treatment of a Wood Preserving Site.* Applications Analysis Report, EPA/540/A5-91/003. USEPA Office of Research and Development (Cincinnati), 1992

US ENVIRONMENTAL PROTECTION AGENCY. *BioTrol Soil Washing System for Treatment of a Wood Preserving Site.* Technology Demonstration Summary. EPA/540/S5-91/003. USEPA Centre for Environmental Research Information (Cincinnati), 1992

US ENVIRONMENTAL PROTECTION AGENCY. *CF Systems Organics Extract Process, New Bedford Harbor, MA*. Applications Analysis Report, EPA/540/A5-90/002. USEPA Office of Research and Development (Washington DC), 1990

US ENVIRONMENTAL PROTECTION AGENCY. *Chemfix Technologies Inc, Solidification/stabilization Process, Clackamas, Oregon, Volume 1*. Technology Evaluation Report, EPA/540/5-89/011a. USEPA (Cincinnati), 1990

US ENVIRONMENTAL PROTECTION AGENCY. *Chemical Dehalogenation Treatment: APEG Treatment*. Engineering Bulletin, EPA/540/2-90/015. USEPA, 1990

US ENVIRONMENTAL PROTECTION AGENCY. Chemical On-site Treatment Utilizing KPEG Process at Wide Beach, New York. In: *Final Report of the NATO/CCMS Study on Innovative Technologies for Clean-up of Contaminated Soil and Groundwater, Volume II, Part 2*. USEPA (Cincinnati), 1993, pp 1259-1297

US ENVIRONMENTAL PROTECTION AGENCY. *Chemical Oxidation Treatment*. Engineering Bulletin, EPA/540/2-91/025. USEPA (Cincinnati), 1991

US ENVIRONMENTAL PROTECTION AGENCY. Chemical Waste Management Inc: DeChlor/KGME Process. In: *The Superfund Innovative Technology Evaluation Program: Technology Profiles*. 5th edition, EPA/540/R-92/077. USEPA (Washington DC), 1991, pp 62-63

US ENVIRONMENTAL PROTECTION AGENCY. Chemical Waste Management, Inc (X-TRAX™ Thermal Desorption). In: *The Superfund Innovative Technology Evaluation Program: Technology Profiles*. 6th edition, EPA/540/R-93/526. USEPA Office of Solid Waste and Emergency Response (Washington DC), 1993, pp 46-47

US ENVIRONMENTAL PROTECTION AGENCY. *Clean Berkshires, Inc. Thermal desorption system*. Site Technology Capsule, EPA/540/R-94/507a. USEPA (Cincinnati), 1994

US ENVIRONMENTAL PROTECTION AGENCY. *Control of air emissions from materials handling during remediation*, EPA/540/2-91/023. USEPA Office of Emergency and Remedial Response (Washington DC), 1991

US ENVIRONMENTAL PROTECTION AGENCY. *Corrective Action: Technologies and Applications*. Seminar Publication, EPA/625/4-89/020. USEPA Centre for Environmental Research Information (Cincinnati), 1989

US ENVIRONMENTAL PROTECTION AGENCY. *Demonstration Plan for the Taciuk Thermal Processor at the Wide Beach Development Site*. Demonstration Program Draft Report, March 1991. USEPA (Cincinnati), 1991

US ENVIRONMENTAL PROTECTION AGENCY. *Design and development of a pilot-scale debris decontamination system*. Technology Evaluation Report, Volume 1. EPA/540/5-91/006a. USEPA Office of Research and Development (Washington DC), 1991

US ENVIRONMENTAL PROTECTION AGENCY. *Emerging Technology Bulletin: Photolysis/Biodegredation of PCB and PCDD/PCDF contaminated soils*. EPA/540/F-94/502. USEPA (Cincinnati), 1994

US ENVIRONMENTAL PROTECTION AGENCY. *EPA Mobile Incineration System Modifications, Testing and Operations – February 1986 to June 1989*. Project Summary, EPA/600/S2-90/042. USEPA Risk Reduction Engineering Laboratory (Cincinnati), 1990

US ENVIRONMENTAL PROTECTION AGENCY. *EPA RREL's mobile volume reduction unit*. Applications Analysis Report, EPA/540/AR-93/508. USEPA Office of Research and Development (Washington DC), 1993

US ENVIRONMENTAL PROTECTION AGENCY. Exxon Chemical Company & Rio Linda Chemical Company: Chemical oxidation and cyanide destruction. In: *The Superfund Innovative Technology Evaluation Program: Technology Profiles*. 5th edition, EPA/540/R-92/077. USEPA (Washington DC), 1991, pp 88-89

US ENVIRONMENTAL PROTECTION AGENCY. *Fate of Polychlorinated Biphenyls (PCBs) in Soil Following Stabilization with Quicklime*. EPA/600/2-91/052. USEPA (Cincinnati), 1991

US ENVIRONMENTAL PROTECTION AGENCY. *Final Report NATO/CCMS Pilot Study: Demonstration of Remedial Action Technologies for Contaminated Land and Groundwater*. EPA/600/R-93/012. USEPA Risk Reduction Engineering Laboratory (Cincinnati), 1993

US ENVIRONMENTAL PROTECTION AGENCY. Gruppo Italimpresse (Infrared thermal destruction) *The Superfund Innovative Technology Evaluation Program: Technology Profiles*. 6th edition, EPA/R-99/526. USEPA Office of Solid Waste and Emergency Response (Washington DC), 1993, pp 68-69

US ENVIRONMENTAL PROTECTION AGENCY. *Guide for conducting treatability studies under CERCLA: Solidification/stabilization*. USEPA, 1993

US ENVIRONMENTAL PROTECTION AGENCY. *Guide for conducting treatability studies under CERCLA: Thermal desorption remedy selection*. EPA/540/R-92/074A. USEPA (Washington DC), 1992

US ENVIRONMENTAL PROTECTION AGENCY. *Guide for Conducting Treatability Studies under CERCLA*. Final, EPA/540/R-92/071a. USEPA Office of Research and Development (Washington DC), 1992

US ENVIRONMENTAL PROTECTION AGENCY. *Handbook for stabilization/solidification of hazardous wastes*. EPA/540/2-86/001. USEPA (Cincinnati), 1986

US ENVIRONMENTAL PROTECTION AGENCY. *Handbook on in situ treatment of hazardous waste-contaminated soil*. EPA/540/2-90/002. USEPA (Cincinnati), 1990

US ENVIRONMENTAL PROTECTION AGENCY. *Handbook: Quality assurance/quality control (QA/QC) for hazardous waste incinerators*. EPA/625/6-89/023. USEPA (Cincinnati), 1991

US ENVIRONMENTAL PROTECTION AGENCY. *HAZCON Solidification Process, Douglassville, PA*. Applications Analysis Report, EPA/540/A5-89/001. USEPA (Cincinnati), 1989

US ENVIRONMENTAL PROTECTION AGENCY. Horsehead Resource Development Co Inc (HRD): Flame reactor. In: *The Superfund Innovative Technology Evaluation Program: Technology Profiles*. 6th edition, EPA/540/R-93/526. USEPA Office of Solid Waste and Emergency Response (Washington DC), 1993, pp 70-71

US ENVIRONMENTAL PROTECTION AGENCY. *Horsehead Resource Development Co. Inc.: Flame reactor technology*. Applications Analysis Report, EPA/540/A5-91/005. USEPA Risk Reduction Engineering Laboratory Office of Research and Development (Cincinnati), 1992

US ENVIRONMENTAL PROTECTION AGENCY. *Innovative Technology: Glycolate Dehalogenation*. Directive 9200.5-245S. USEPA, 1989

US ENVIRONMENTAL PROTECTION AGENCY. *Innovative Treatment Technologies, Overview and Guide to Information Sources*. EPA/540/9-91/002. USEPA, Office of Solid Waste and Emergency Response (Washington DC), 1991

US ENVIRONMENTAL PROTECTION AGENCY. Institute of Gas Technology: Chemical and biological treatment. In: *The Superfund Innovative Technology Evaluation Program: Technology Profiles*. 5th edition, EPA/540/R-92/077. USEPA (Washington DC), 1991, pp 258-259

US ENVIRONMENTAL PROTECTION AGENCY. *Mobile/Transportable Incineration Treatment*. Engineering Bulletin, EPA/540/2-90/014. USEPA Office of Emergency and Remedial Response (Washington DC), 1990

US ENVIRONMENTAL PROTECTION AGENCY. Ogden Environmental Services (Circulating bed combuster) In: *The Superfund Innovative Technology Evaluation Program: Technology Profiles*. 5th edition, EPA/540/R-92/077. USEPA Office of Solid Waste and Emergency Response (Washington DC), 1992, pp 122-123

US ENVIRONMENTAL PROTECTION AGENCY. *Physical/chemical treatment technology resource guide*. EPA/542/B-94/008. USEPA Office of Solid Waste and Emergency Response Technology Innovation Office (Washington DC), 1994

US ENVIRONMENTAL PROTECTION AGENCY. Retech Inc (Plasma Arc Vitrification). In: *The Superfund Innovative Technology Evaluation Program: Technology Profiles*. 6th edition, EPA/540/R-93/526. USEPA Office of Solid Waste and Emergency Response (Washington DC), 1993, pp 88-89

US ENVIRONMENTAL PROTECTION AGENCY. *Retech, Inc.,Plasma Centrifugal Furnace*, Applications Analysis Report, EPA/540/A5-91/007. USEPA Risk Reduction Engineering Laboratory Office of Research and Development (Cincinnati), 1992

US ENVIRONMENTAL PROTECTION AGENCY. *Shirco Infrared Incineration System*. Applications Analysis Report, EPA/540/A5-89/010. USEPA (Cincinnati), 1989

US ENVIRONMENTAL PROTECTION AGENCY. *Silicate Technology Corporation's Solidification Technology for Organic and Inorganic Contaminants in Soils*. Applications Analysis Report, EPA/540/AR-92/010. USEPA (Cincinnati), 1992

US ENVIRONMENTAL PROTECTION AGENCY. *Slurry biodegradation*. Engineering Bulletin, EPA/540/2-90/016. USEPA Office of Emergency and Remedial Response (Washington DC), 1990

US ENVIRONMENTAL PROTECTION AGENCY. *Slurry biodegradation: International Technology Corporation.* Demonstration Bulletin, EPA/540/M5-91/009. USEPA Centre for Environmental Research Information (Cincinnati), 1992

US ENVIRONMENTAL PROTECTION AGENCY. *Slurry-phase biodegradation.* Innovative Technology Report, Directive 9200 5-25. USEPA Solid Waste and Emergency Response, 1981

US ENVIRONMENTAL PROTECTION AGENCY. *Soil/sediment washing system.* Demonstration Bulletin, EPA/540/MR-92/075. USEPA Centre for Environmental Research Information (Cincinnati), 1992

US ENVIRONMENTAL PROTECTION AGENCY. *Soil Washing Treatment.* Engineering Bulletin, EPA/540/2-90/017. USEPA Office of Engineering and Remedial Response (Washington DC), 1990

US ENVIRONMENTAL PROTECTION AGENCY. *Solidification/stabilization and its application to waste materials.* EPA/530/R-93/012. USEPA (Washington DC), 1993

US ENVIRONMENTAL PROTECTION AGENCY. *Solidification/stabilization of organics and inorganics.* Engineering Bulletin, EPA/540/S-92/015. USEPA (Cincinnati), 1993

US ENVIRONMENTAL PROTECTION AGENCY. *Soliditech Inc, Solidification/stabilization Process.* Applications Analysis Report, EPA/540/A5-89/005. USEPA (Cincinnati), 1990

US ENVIRONMENTAL PROTECTION AGENCY. *Solvent Extraction Treatment* Engineering Bulletin, EPA/540/2-90/013. USEPA Office of Emergency and Remedial Response (Washington DC), 1990

US ENVIRONMENTAL PROTECTION AGENCY. *Stabilization/solidification of CERCLA and RCRA wastes: Physical tests, chemical testing procedures, technology screening and field activities.* EPA/625/6-89/022. USEPA (Cincinnati), 1989

US ENVIRONMENTAL PROTECTION AGENCY. *Superfund Fact Sheet Update: Koppers Inc., North Carolina.* USEPA Region 4 (Atlanta), 1993

US ENVIRONMENTAL PROTECTION AGENCY. Supplementary Information on the APEG Process, Wide Beach, New York. In: *Final Report of the NATO/CCMS Study on Innovative Technologies for the Clean up of Contaminated Soils and Groundwater, Volume 2, Part 2.* EPA/600/R-93/012c. USEPA (Cincinnati), 1993, pp 1259-1287

US ENVIRONMENTAL PROTECTION AGENCY. *Survey of Materials – Handling Technologies used at Hazardous Waste Sites.* EPA/540/2-91/010. USEPA Office of Research and Development (Washington DC), 1991

US ENVIRONMENTAL PROTECTION AGENCY. *Technology Screening Guide for Treatment of CERCLA Soils and Sludges.* EPA/540//2-88/004. USEPA, Office of Solid Waste and Emergency Response, Office of Emergency and Remedial Response, (Washington DC), 1988

US ENVIRONMENTAL PROTECTION AGENCY. *The Carver-Greenfield ProcessR Dehydro-Tech Corporation.* Applications Analysis Report, EPA/540/AR-92/002. USEPA Office of Research and Development (Washington DC), 1992

US ENVIRONMENTAL PROTECTION AGENCY. *The Superfund Innovative Technology Evaluation Program. Technology Profiles,* 5th edition, EPA/540/R-92/077. USEPA Office of Solid Waste and Emergency Response (Washington DC), 1992

US ENVIRONMENTAL PROTECTION AGENCY. *Thermal desorption applications manual for treating petroleum contaminated soils.* Contractors report in pre-publication review. USEPA (Edison NJ), August 1993

US ENVIRONMENTAL PROTECTION AGENCY. *Thermal Desorption Treatment.* Engineering Bulletin, EPA/540/2-91/008. USEPA Office of Emergency and Remedial Response (Washington DC), 1991

VERHEUL, J.H. *et al.* Biological remediation of contaminated land: A Dutch perspective. In: *Proceedings of a Conference on Contaminated Land.* Institution of Chemical Engineers (London), 1993

WILES, C. A review of solidification/stabilisation technology. *Journal of Hazardous Materials,* 1987, 14, pp 5-21

WOOLLINS, J.M. Soils washing: Cost minimisation through volume reduction. In: *Proceedings of a Conference on Contaminated Land Policy, Economics and Technology.* Paper No. 6. IBC Technical Services (London), February 1993

INDEX

Note: Numbers in italics refer to Tables. B indicates a Box, and Ap indicates an Appendix

air pollution control (APC) 33
Air Quality Regulations (1989) 11
Alberta Oil Sands Technology and
  Research Authority 162Ap
aliphatic hydrocarbons, metabolic
  pathways for 100B
alkali polyethylene glycol (APEG)
  process
  applicability 155Ap
  block diagram *164*Ap
  costs 157-8Ap
  effectiveness 157Ap
  environmental protection 156Ap
  health and safety 156-7Ap
  information requirements 157Ap
  laboratory support 156Ap
  limitations 157Ap
  plant and equipment 156Ap
  principle 89-90, *89*, 153-5Ap
  prognosis 158Ap
  site requirements 156Ap
  technological variations 158Ap

alkaline hydrolysis of cyanides 87
Alternative Treatment Technology Centre
  (ATTIC) 3
Anaerobic thermal processor (ATP)
  (SoilTech)
    demonstration project 162-3Ap, *165*Ap
    project/operating costs *41*
anthrax 93
APEG *see* alkali polyethylene glycol
  (APEG) process
Applications Analysis Reports (USEPA
  Office of Research and Development) 3
aromatic hydrocarbons, metabolic
  pathways for 101B
asphalt emulsions solidification process
  137-9
ATEG process 154Ap
  schematic diagram *155*Ap

base-catalysed decomposition process
  (BCDP)
    effectiveness 160Ap

principle 89, *89*, 158Ap
US Navy/Batelle process 159-60Ap
beds, biological treatment *see* treatment
  beds, biological
bentonite stabilisation *130*
Bergmann bv soil washing system 56B
biological methods
  aliphatic hydrocarbons, metabolic
    pathways 100B
  applicability *6*, 102-3
  aromatic hydrocarbons, metabolic
    pathways 101B
  bioreactors 109-10
  costs 119-20
  effectiveness 115-18
  environmental protection 113
  ·health and safety 113
  information requirements 114-15
  laboratory support 112
  limitations 118, 119B
  plant and equipment 113, *114*
  principle and dangers 99-100
  prognosis 120
  site requirements 110-13
  treatment beds 100, *102*, 103-9
  see also bioreactors, dry; bioreactors,
    slurry
bioreactors, dry
  for oil 109B
  principle/characteristics 100, *102*, 109-
    10
  stage processes 109
bioreactors, slurry
  for creosote contaminated soil 111B
  principle/characteristics 100, *102*
  Remediation Technologies Inc process
    110B
  site requirements *112*
Biotecknisk Jordens (DK), monitoring
  and validation *13*
BioTrol (US)
  aqueous treatment system (BATS)
    using biological treatment 58B
  monitoring and validation *13*
  soil washing system using attrition and
    classification 54B
bitumen solidification process 138-9

Cacitox treatment process 79B
cement based stabilisation 123, 124B,
  127, *128*, 129-39, 169Ap
  see also stabilisation and solidification
centrifuges *8*
CF Systems Corp, liquified gases use 70B
Chemfix Technologies

stabilising/solidifying process 133B
chemical disinfection 93
chemical fixation 123
chemical treatment methods
  applicability 6, 78-82
  costs 96
  dechlorination reactions 89-92
  effectiveness 96
  health and safety 95
  hydrolysis 87-93
  information requirements 95-6
  laboratory support 95
  limitations 96, 97B
  oxidation 83-7, 83B
  plant and equipment 93, *94*
  polymerisation 92
  principle 78, 82-3
  prognosis 96
  quality management for 95
  reduction 87-9
  site requirements *93*
  soil properties effects 97B
  see also alkali polyethylene glycol
    (APEG) process; base-catalysed
    decomposition process (BCDP)
chlorine dioxide, as an oxidising agent 86
chromatographic equipment, liquid/gas
  monitoring 113
chromium, hexavalent, reduction of 88-9
civil engineering 12
classification of ex-situ methods *2*
clay
  creosote-contaminated *38*
  organophilic, binders 134-6, *137*
compliance testing 12
corrosives, examples of elements 151Ap,
  152Ap
costs
  anaerobic thermal processor *41*
  APEG process 157-8Ap
  biological methods 119-20
  chemical treatment methods 96
  cyclones *40*
  Hazcon stabilisation/solidification
    system 146
  incineration *40*
  infra-red thermal treatment *40*
  rotary kiln incinerators *40*
  soil washing systems 64-5, 66-7B
  solvent extraction *74*
  stabilisation and solidification 145-6,
    146
  thermal desorption *41*
  thermal methods 39-41, *40*
crushers 10

cyanide
    destruction of, oxidation treatment 87B
    examples of elements 151Ap, 152Ap
cyclones *8*
    costs data *40*
    vitrification performance *38*

Davy International, leach/in-pulp process
    80B, 81B
debris, treatment information needs *35*
DeChlor/KGME process *89*, 92
dechlorination reactions *see* alkali
    polyethylene glycol (APEG); base-
    catalysed decomposition process
    (BCDP)
dechlorination reactions
    alkali polyethylene glycol (APEG)
      process 89-90, *89*
    base-catalysed decomposition (BCDP)
      process *89*, 90
    DeChlor/KGME process *89*, 92
    detoxifying PCBs 89
    sodium borohydride process *89*, 92
Deconterra soil washing process 54B
Dehydro-Tech Corp, solvent extraction
    69B
desorption *see* thermal desorption
destruction/removal efficiencies (DREs)
    36
dewatering 9-10
dioxins/furans, examples of elements
    151Ap
disinfection, chemical treatment 93
Dispersion by Chemical Reaction (DCR)
    135B
distillates, middle, degradation on
    treatment beds *116*
drying 10
Duty of Care 11

ECO-LOGIC process 42B
Ecotechniek (NL), monitoring and
    validation *13*
effectiveness
    biological methods 115-18
    chemical treatment methods 96
    definition 5
    destruction/removal 5
    incineration 34, 36
    and limiting factors 5
    oxidation treatment *84*
    soil washing systems 60-3
    solvent extraction 72-3
    stabilisation and solidification 142-3
    thermal desorption 34, 36

treatment 5-7
electro-remediation 74-6
electrophilic binders 135
Engineering Bulletins (USEPA Office of
    Emergency and Remedial Response) 3
environmental protection
    alkali polyethylene glycol (APEG)
      process 156Ap
    biological methods 113
    legal aspects 11
    mitigating measures 33
    soil washing systems 57-9
    solvent extraction 71
    stabilisation and solidification 141
    thermal methods 33
Environmental Protection Act (EPA)
    (1990) 11
EXCEL soil treatment process (BNFL)
    79B

flotation separation techniques 48B
fluidised bed incinerators
    bubbling 25
    circulating 25, *26*, 27B
    information needs for *35*

gas collection and treatment, for thermal
    desorption 23-4
Geo-Con (US), monitoring and validation
    13
Guam, base-catalysed decomposition
    process (BCDP) application 159-60Ap

halogenated/non-halogenated
    volatiles/semivolatiles, examples of
    elements 150Ap
harbour sediments, liquified gas
    treatment *72*
Hazcon stabilisation/solidification system
    136B
    costs 146
health and safety
    alkali polyethylene glycol (APEG)
      process 156-7Ap
    biological methods 113
    chemical treatment methods 95
    legal aspects 11
    soil washing systems 59
    solvent extraction 71
    and thermal methods 34
hydrocarbon carrier oil system, solvent
    extraction 69B
hydrocyclones *8*
    separation technique 48B
hydrogen peroxide, as an oxidising agent

85-6, 85B, 86B
hydrolysis 87
    alkaline hydrolysis of cyanides 87
    and oxidation treatment *84*

incineration
    applicability *6*, *18*, 19
    atmospheric emissions *33*
    costs *40*
    direct-fired rotary kiln 24, *25*, *26*
    effectiveness 34, 36
    fluidised beds 25, *26*
    information needs for *35*
    infra-red systems 27, 28B
    limitations 39B
    performance data in US *37*
    principle 16, 24
information sources, remediation
    methods *3*
infra-red incinerators *26*, 27, 28B
    cost data *40*
    information needs for *35*
inorganic contaminants, thermal
    treatment methods *18*

jigging *8*

Klöckner Oecotec GmbH soil washing
    system 53B
KPEG process 153Ap
KTEG process 154Ap, 155Ap

laboratory facilities 12
laboratory support
    alkali polyethylene glycol (APEG)
        process 156Ap
    biological methods 112
    chemical treatment methods 95
leach/in-pulp decontamination process
    80B, 81B
legal aspects 11
lime-based stabilisation 134
liquids
    classification of ex-situ methods *2*
    contaminated, treatment trains for 14
liquified gas treatment
    harbour sediments *72*
    refinery sludges *73*
Lurgi GmbH soil washing system *13*, 54B
magnetic separation techniques *8*, 48B
materials, contaminated types of *7*
metals
    leachable, stabilisation 123
    non-volatile, examples of elements
        152Ap

volatile, examples of elements 152Ap
monitoring 12-13
    chromatographic equipment, liquid/gas
        113
    stabilisation and solidification 170-
        1Ap

on-site treatment 3-4
open composting system, biological
    treatment 108B
operational requirements 12
organic contaminants
    oxidation treatment *85*
    reduction treatment 88
    thermal treatment methods *18*
organic polymer based stabilisation *128*
organics, examples of elements 150-1Ap
owner/operator responsibility 11
oxidation treatment
    application 83-4
    cyanide destruction 87B
    effectiveness *84*
    and hydrolysis *84*
    organic compounds *85*
    oxidising agents 85-7
    soil catalysed 86, 87B
oxidisers, examples of elements 152Ap
ozone, as an oxidising agent 85

particle size separation, technique 48B
PCBs *see* polychlorinated biphenyl
    (PCBs) contamination
performance checking 12
pesticide contamination, triethylamine
    extraction method *72*
pesticides, examples of elements 151Ap
phanerachate chrysosporium 108
physical treatment methods
    applications *6*
    electro-remediation 74-6
    flotation 48B
    hydrocycloning 48B
    magnetic techniques 48B
    particle size separation 48B
    principle 47
    separation techniques summary 8, *8*, *9*
    settling velocity separation 48B
    specific gravity separation 48B
    see also soil washing systems; solvent
        extraction
planning and development control 11
planning and management 12
plant and equipment
    alkali polyethylene glycol (APEG)
        process 156Ap

biological methods 113
chemical treatment methods 93
for size reduction of material 10
stabilisation and solidification 139, *140*
thermal methods 30, *32*
plasma-arc vitrification 29B
polychlorinated biphenyl (PCBs)
contamination
base catalysed hydrogenation 90
cement kiln dust treatment 144B
chemical dechlorination 89-92
DeChlor/KGME process *89*
examples of elements 151Ap
problem with, explanation 91B
sodium borohydride process *89*
thermal treatment 17
Wide Beach demonstration treatment
plant 161-3Ap
see also alkali polyethylene glycol
(APEG) process; base-catalysed
decomposition process (BCDP)
polymerisation chemical treatment 92
Portland cement stabilisation *see* cement-
based stabilisation
post-treatment
equipment for chemical *94*
validation *13*
Pozzolans with lime or cement
stabilisation *127, 128*
pre-treatment 8
equipment for chemical *94*
soil washing systems 49, *58*
thermal desorption 19
process monitoring *see* monitoring
public health, legal aspects 11

radioactive materials, examples of
elements 152Ap
reactive contaminants, thermal treatment
methods *18*
reducer contaminant elements 152Ap
reduction
hexavalent chromium 88-9
for organic compound treatment 88
organic compounds, reactions of iron
with 88
principle 87-8
reductive dehalogenation 88
selenium, reducing agents for 89
refinery sludges, liquified gas treatment
73
refinery wastes, degradation on treatment
beds *116*
Resource Guides, listing USEPA

publications 3
Resources Conservation Company 68B
rotary kiln incinerators 24, *25, 26*
cost data *40*
information needs *35*

SCG (NL), monitoring and validation *13*
screening *8*
selenium, reducing agents for 89
separation techniques *see* physical
treatment methods
settling velocity separation 48B
shredders 10
site requirements
alkali polyethylene glycol (APEG)
process 156
biological methods 110-13
chemical treatment methods *93*
soil washing systems *57*
stabilisation and solidification *139,
140*
thermal methods 30, *32*
slag based stabilisation 132-4
sludges, treatment information needs *35*
slurry phase biodegradation 110B
for creosote contaminated soil 111B
sodium borohydride process *89, 92, 92B*
soil bank biological treatment beds 107B
soil catalysed oxidation treatment 86,
87B
soil washing systems
applicability *6,* 48-50, *49*
with attrition and classification 54B
biological treatment for liquid effluents
58B
chemical characterisation data *60*
with classification and density
separation *55,* 56B
costs 64-5, 66-7B
effectiveness 60-3
environmental protection 57-9
equipment requirements *58*
health and safety 59
information requirements 59
limitations *64*
metal characterisation data *60*
method descriptions 50-6
performance data for *61-2, 63*
physical characterisation data *60*
plant components 52
pre-treatment 49, *58*
processing steps 52
prognosis 65
schematic of process *50*
site requirements *57*

with steam injection 53B
soils, treatment information needs *35*
SoilTech Anaerobic Thermal processor
  (ATP) process 163Ap
solidification
  principle 122-3
  see also stabilisation and solidification
Soliditech Inc stabilisation process 138B
solids, classification of ex-situ methods *2*
solvent extraction
  applicability *6*, *67*, 68
  costs *74*
  effectiveness 72-3
  environmental protection 71
  health and safety 71
  hydrocarbon carrier oil system 69B
  information requirements 71, *72*
  limitations 73
  liquified gas system 70B
  method description 68-71
  operational requirements 71
  principle 65
  prognosis 73-4
  triethylamine system 68B
  wastewaters 71
specific gravity separation 48B
stabilisation and solidification
  applicability *6*, 126, *126*
    factors identified by vendors 169Ap
  bentonite *130*
  cement stabilisation *127*, 129
    with additives 129
    interaction with chemical groups
    130
  cement-based systems 123-4, 124B,
    127, *128*
    for PCB contamination 144B
    for steel works sludge 145B
  Chemfix Technologies
    stabilising/solidifying process 133B
  chemical fixation 123
  clay, organophilic, binders 134-6, *137*
  compatibility of techniques *128*
  costs 145-6, *146*
  curing pumpable material 125-6
  direct mixing 124
  effectiveness 142-3
  environmental protection 141
  in-drum processing 125
  information requirements 141-2, *142*
  leachable metals 123
  lime-based methods/techniques *128*,
    134
  limitations 144-5
  monitoring and testing 170-1Ap

  organic binders 124
  organic polymer based *128*
  plant and equipment 139, *140*
  plant processing 124, 125
  Pozzolans with lime or cement *127*,
    129-32, *131*
  pozzolans and vitreous slags 132B
  principle 122-3
  prognosis 147
  sampling and testing 170-1Ap
  site requirements *139*, *140*
  slag based 132-4
  thermoplastic based *127*, *128*, 137-9
  treatability testing/studies 142, 143
steel works sludge, cement based
  solidification 145B
sweep gas 23B

tabling *8*
Technology Evaluation Reports (USEPA
  Risk Reduction Engineering
  Laboratory) 3
thermal desorption
  applicability *6*, *18*
  atmospheric emissions *33*
  classification of systems of *20*
  conveyer systems for 22
  costs *41*
  direct heated processes 20-2, *21*
  effectiveness 34, 36
  gas collection and treatment 23-4
  heated shell *23*
  indirect heated processes 22-3
  information needs for *35*
  limitations 39B
  performance data *37*
    creosote-contaminated clay *38*
  pre-treatment 19
  principle 16, 19
  rotary units for 22
  thermal screws for 23B
  TRAX system 168Ap
thermal destruction *see* incineration
thermal methods
  absorption 17
  applicability *6*, 17-19
  costs 39-41
  effectiveness 34-6
  environmental protection 33
  health and safety for 34
  information requirements 34, *35*
  limitations 36, *39*
  plant and equipment 30
  principles of 16-17
  prognosis 42-3

site requirements 30
see also incineration; thermal
    desorption; vitrification
thermal screws 23B
thermoplastics, stabilisation with *127,
    128*, 137-9
transformer oils/carcasses 17
TRAX thermal desorption system 168Ap
treatability testing/studies 142, 143
treatment
    applicability of methods 4-5, *6*
    effectiveness 5-7
    limiting factors 5
    treatability studies 4
treatment beds, biological
    characteristics *102*
    for chlorinated aliphatic hydrocarbons
        104
    for chlorinated phenols, benzene and
        their pesticide derivatives *104*
    engineered soil banks 107B
    for non-halogenated solvents *104*
    open composting system 108B
    for petrochemicals and coal gas
        products *104*
    polyaromatic hydrocarbons,
        temperature effects *107*
    principle 100, 103, 105-6
    temperature dependence 106-7
    white rot fungi 108-9
treatment trains 13-14
triethylamine system solvent extraction
    68B
performance *72*

US Environmental Protection Agency
    (USEPA) 5, 34, 142
USEPA SITE Demonstration programme
    42

Vendor Information System for
    Innovative Treatment Technologies
    (VISITT) 3
vitrification
    adapted glass-making technology 31B
    applicability *6, 18*
    atmospheric emissions *33*
    cyclone unit performance *38*
    electrically heated 30B
    information needs for *35*
    limitations 39B
    plasma-arc 29B
    principle 16, 17, 28-9
    prognosis 42
    waste oil fired 30B
volatisation 116

wash solutions, reconditioning 13-14
washing systems *see* soil washing
    systems
wastewaters, solvent extraction 71
Water Industry Act (1991) 11
Water Resources Act (1991) 11
Waukegan Harbour Superfund site, PCBs
    163Ap
wet oxidation 86
white rot fungi, for biological treatment
    100, 108-9
Wide Beach demonstration treatment
    plant, PCB contamination 161-3Ap
wood treatment sludges/wastes
    in slurry bioreactor *117*
    in tank reactor *118*

8 Volume VIII In-situ remedial methods for contaminated groundwater and other liquids SP108

Volume VIII describes the main generic methods available for the treatment of contaminated groundwater (following extraction from the ground) and other liquids (including for example leachates, contaminated surface water, process effluents etc.).

Most available techniques are based on conventional water and wastewater treatment technologies adapted as appropriate for use in contaminated land applications. This may present a number of design and implementation problems, such as the need to modify proprietary systems for smaller-scale and (typically) more temporary applications, as well as flexibility in the treatment system to accommodate changes in the nature and concentrations of contaminants as treatment progresses.

Issues that should be addressed during design and implementation, summary descriptions of the main treatment options and case study examples of treatment systems used in contaminated land applications are presented.

CONTENTS

1 INTRODUCTION
    1.1 Background
    1.2 Design aspects
    1.3 Legal aspects
    1.4 Operational aspects
    References

2 TREATMENT METHODS
    2.1 Introduction
    2.2 Chemical treatment
    2.3 Coagulation and flocculation
    2.4 Biological treatment
    2.5 Filtration
    2.6 Air stripping
    2.7 Carbon adsorption
    2.8 Sorption of organic compounds
    2.9 Advanced tertiary treatment techniques
    2.10 Biorecovery of metals from groundwater
    References

3 TREATMENT TRAINS AND CASE STUDIES

3.1   Introduction
3.2   Typical treatment trains
3.3   Case studies
References

REFERENCES

ANON. The CO_2 route to effective pH control. *Water and Waste Treatment*, October, 1992

CHILDS, K.A. Treatment of contaminated groundwater. In: *Contaminated Land* SMITH, M.A. (ed.) Plenum Press (London), 1985, pp 183-197

CHILDS, K.A. Treatment of contaminated groundwater. In: *Contaminated land: reclamation and treatment.* Smith, M.A. (ed.) Plenum (London), 1985, pp 183-1198

DE BRUIJN, P. Biotreatment in soil remediation. In: *Proceedings of a Conference on Contaminated Land Policy, Regulation and Technology.* IBC (London), 1992. Paper No. 10

ENVIRONMENT CANADA. *Proceedings of a Conference on Advanced Oxidation Processes for the Treatment of Contaminated Water and Air.* Environment Canada (Toronto), 1990

EUROPEAN WATER POLLUTION CONTROL ASSOCIATION. *European design and operations guidelines for reed bed treatment systems.* Report prepared for European Commission/EWPCA Emergent Hydrophyte Treatment Systems Expert Contact Group (Cooper P.F. ed.), 1990

LEWIS, N. Development of emerging technologies within the SITE program. In: *Proceedings of a Conference on Contaminated Land Policy, Regulation and Technology.* IBC (London), 1992, Paper No. 10

LEWIS, N. Soil vapour extraction technologies. In: *Final Report NATO/CCMS Pilot Study on Demonstration of Remedial Action Technologies for Contaminated Land and Groundwater, Volume 1.* EPA/600/R-93/012a. USEPA Risk Reduction Engineering Laboratory (Cincinnati), 1993, pp33-52

MUELLER, J.G. *et al.* Remediation of groundwater contaminated with organic wood preservatives using biological treatment technologies. In: *Proceedings of an International Symposium on Environmental Contamination in Central and Eastern Europe.* Florida State University and Technical University of Budapest, 1992, pp 819-821

NYER, E.K. Biological treatment of a groundwater contaminated with phenol. In: *Groundwater Treatment Technology.* Nyer, E.K. (ed.) Van Nostrand Reinhold (New York), 1992, pp 272-270

NYER, E.K. *Groundwater Treatment Technology.* Second edition. Van Nostrand Reinhold (New York), 1992

PAINE, G.G. Removal of VOCs from fractured bedrock groundwater. *Hazardous Materials Control,* 1992, 5 (3), 40-46

ROBINSON, H.D., BARR, M.J., FORMBY, B.W., and MOAG, A. *The treatment of landfill leachates using reed bed systems.* Paper to the Annual Training Day on Planning and Engineering for Sustainable Landfill Management. IWEM (Central Southern Branch), October 1992

SCHMIDT, J.W. Pump and treatment groundwater. In: *Final Report to the Committee on the Challenges of Modern Society Pilot Study on Demonstration of Remedial Action Technologies for Contaminated Land and Groundwater, Volume 1.* USEPA Risk Reduction Engineering Laboratory (Cincinnati), 1993, pp 65-76

SINGLETON, I. and TOBIN, J. Meet the metal-loving microbes. *Technology Ireland,* 1994, February, 39-42

SMITH, M.A. International study of technologies for cleaning up contaminated land and groundwater. In: *Proceedings of a Conference Land Rec '88.* Durham County Council (Durham), 1988, pp 259-266

Standard handbook of environmental engineering. Corbitt, R.A. (ed.) McGraw-Hill (New York), 1989

STAPS, S. Microbial treatment technologies. In: *Final Report to the Committee on the Challenges of Modern Society Pilot Study on Demonstration of Remedial Action Technologies for Contaminated Land and Groundwater, Volume 1.* EPA/600/R-93/012a. USEPA Risk Reduction Engineering Laboratory (Cincinnati), 1993, pp 86-95

ULLENSVANG, B. Design and construction of an on-site treatment plant at the Operating Industries Inc. landfill. In: *Proceedings of the First International Meeting, NATO/CCMS Pilot study on Evaluation of Demonstrated and Emerging Technologies for the treatment and clean-up of contaminated land and groundwater.* Budapest, 1992

URLINGS, L.G.C.M. *et al.* Biological treatment of groundwater polluted with HCH, chlorobenzene and benzene on a former pesticide production site in Bunschoten, the Netherlands. In: *Final Report to the Committee on the Challenges of Modern Society Pilot Study on demonstration of Remedial Action Technologies for Contaminated Land and Groundwater, Volume 2 – Part 2.* EPA/600/R-93/012a. US EPA Risk Reduction Engineering Laboratory (Cincinnati), 1993, pp 1350-1361

URLINGS, L.G.C.M. *et al.* In situ cadmium removal. In: *Final Report Committee on the Challenges of Modern Society Pilot Study on Demonstration of Remedial Action Technologies for Contaminated Land and Groundwater, Volume 2 – Part 2.* EPA/600/R-93/012c. USEPA Risk Reduction Engineering Laboratory (Cincinnati), 1993, pp 1135-1156

US ENVIRONMENTAL PROTECTION AGENCY. *Biotrol soil washing system for the treatment of a wood preserving site.* Applications Analysis Report, EPA/540/A5-91/003. USEPA Risk Reduction and Engineering Laboratory/Office of Research and Development (Cincinnati), 1992

US ENVIRONMENTAL PROTECTION AGENCY. *Chemical Treatment and Ultrafiltration System, Palmerton Pennsylvania.* Technology Demonstration Summary, EPA/540/F-002. USEPA, Center for Environmental Research Information (Cincinnati), 1992

US ENVIRONMENTAL PROTECTION AGENCY. *Constructed Wetlands Treatment for Toxic Metal Contaminated Waters*. Emerging Technology Bulletin, EPA/540/F-92/001. USEPA Center for Environmental Research Information (Cincinnati), 1992

US ENVIRONMENTAL PROTECTION AGENCY. *Corrective Action: Technologies and Applications*. Seminar Publication, EPA/625/4-89/020. USEPA Center for Environmental Research Information (Cincinnati), 1989, Chapter 5

US ENVIRONMENTAL PROTECTION AGENCY. *Demonstration Bulletin: PO*WW*ER™ wastewater treatment system*. EPA/540/MR-93/506. USEPA Risk Reduction Engineering Laboratory (Cincinnati), 1992

US ENVIRONMENTAL PROTECTION AGENCY. *DuPont/Oberlin Microfiltration System, Palmerton, Pennsylvania*. Technology Demonstration Summary, EPA/540/S5-90/007. USEPA Center for Environmental Research Information (Cincinnati), 1992

US ENVIRONMENTAL PROTECTION AGENCY. *Emerging technologies: Bio recovery systems: Removal and recovery of metal ions from grounwater*. EPA/540/5-90/005a. USEPA Office of Research and Development (Washington DC), 1990

US ENVIRONMENTAL PROTECTION AGENCY. EXXON Chemical Company and Rio Linda Chemical Company: Chemical oxidation. In: *The Superfund Innovative Technology Evaluation Program: Technology Profiles*. 5th Edition, EPA/540/R-92/077. USEPA Office of Solid Waste and Emergency Response/Office of Research and Development (Washington DC), 1992, pp 88-89

US ENVIRONMENTAL PROTECTION AGENCY. *Innovative treatment technologies: Overview and guide to information sources*. EPA/540/9-91/002. USEPA Office of Solid Waste and Emergency Response (Washington DC), 1991

US ENVIRONMENTAL PROTECTION AGENCY. *Membrane treatment of wood preserving site groundwater by SBP Technologies Inc*. Applications Analysis Report, EPA/540/AR-92/014. USEPA (Washington DC)

US ENVIRONMENTAL PROTECTION AGENCY. *Microfiltration technology*. Demonstration Bulletin, EPA/540/MR-93/513. USEPA Risk Reduction Engineering Laboratory (Cincinnati), 1993

US ENVIRONMENTAL PROTECTION AGENCY. *Peroxidation Systems Inc. perox-pure™ chemical oxidation technology*. Technology Demonstration Summary, EPA/540/SR-93/501. USEPA Risk Reduction Engineering Laboratory (Cincinnati), 1993

US ENVIRONMENTAL PROTECTION AGENCY. *Ultrox International: Ultraviolet radiation/oxidation technology*. Applications Analysis Report, EPA/540/A5/012. USEPA Office of Research and Development (Washington DC), 1990

INDEX

Note: Numbers in italics refer to Tables. B indicates a Box, and Ap indicates an Appendix

abstraction and discharge permissions 5
acid reagents 10
activated carbon polishing 34
activated sludge 13
activated sludge treatment 34, 35
adsorption, reversible 21
air stripping 18-20, 32, 33, 35
  example of application 20B
  packed towers 18, 33, 34
alkaline chlorination 30
alkaline reagents 10
aquifer contamination, Ville Mercier case
  32-4

bacteria, in Ville Mercier system 33
biofilters 38
biological treatment 12-16
  advantages/disadvantages of different
    systems *14*
  aerobic or anaerobic 12-13, 15
  constructed wetlands treatment for
    contaminated waters 16B
  factors involved 13
  fixed film systems 13-14
    fixed film/activated sludge system
      (FAST™) 35
    submerged aerobic fixed-film
      reactor 15B
  of groundwater contaminated with
    phenol 35-6
  hybrid systems 14
  powder activated carbon treatment
    (PACT™) 15
  suspended systems 13
bioreactors 36-7, 38
  slurry bioreactors 14

carbon adsorption 32, 33
  polishing carbon adsorption step 35
  removal of substances from drinking
    water 20-1
carbon adsorption column 35
case studies 32-8, *39*
  biological pretreatment of groundwater
    using rotating biological contactor
    37-8, *39*
  biological treatment of groundwater
    contaminated with phenol 35-6
  remediation of groundwater
    contaminated with organic wood

preservatives, biological and physical
    treatment 36-7
  treatment of groundwater containing
    chlorinated hydrocarbons, Ville
    Mercier, Canada 32-4
  treatment of hazardous waste landfill
    leachate, California 34
catalytic converters 19B
chemical oxidation/cyanide destruction
  9B
chemical treatments
  neutralisation 8
  operational aspects 10
  oxidation 9-10
  precipitation 8-9
  reduction 10
  UV radiation/oxidation 10, *11*
chlorinated solvents
  removal by carbon adsorption 20
  treatment by UV radiation/oxidation
    11
coagulation 12, 33
contaminants
  mixtures and concentrations in
    contaminated waters 1
  principal, Ville Mercier site *32*
  stripped
    destroyed using thermal oxidation
      19, 19B
    released/collected/destroyed 18-19
contaminated groundwater
  pre-treatment 2, 20
  some techniques/disposal options 2
contaminated land projects, short-term
  nature of, potential design problems of
  treatment train 4-5
contaminated waters, ex-situ treatment of
  1-6
  main operational aspects to be
    considered 6
cyanide, treatment with hydrogen
  peroxide 30
cyanide-bearing wastewaters, membrane
  microfiltration 23-4B

diffusion aeration 34
Duty of Care requirements 5

effluents, high metal loadings reduced by
  chemical precipitation 8-9

Environmental Protection Act (EPA)
(1990) 5

Fenton's Reagent 9
ferrous iron, oxidisation of 9
filtration 17
    classification of filters *17*
    fabric cross-flow filter (EXXFLOW™)
        22, 25B
    see also microfiltration: hyperfiltration
filtration systems 17-18
    backwash highly contaminated 17-18
fixed film systems 13-14
    fixed film/activated sludge system
        (FAST™) 35
    submerged aerobic fixed-film reactor
        15B
flocculation 12, 33
fouling
    in air stripping, bacterial and iron
        oxide 20
    of treatment systems 3

granular filter media 17
granulated activated carbon 34
groundwater
    biological pretreatment of using
        rotating biological contactor 37-8, *39*
    contaminated with organic wood
        preservatives, biological and physical
        treatment 36-7
    see also contaminated groundwater
groundwater treatment
    application of AlgaSORB™ 25B
    systems 2
groundwater water remediation, ex-situ
    treatment 1

health and safety
    requirements 5
    and treatment chemicals 10
heavy metals
    membrane microfiltration 23-4B
    use of precipitation treatment 8
heavy metals/cyanide removal 30, *31*
hexavalent chromium
    reduction of 30
    removal 29, *30*
hydrogen peroxide, oxidation agent 10
hyperfiltration 36-7

ion exchange 22
    operational problems with use of 24
    using zeolite 31
ion exchange resins, selectivity of *24*

iron, can cause problem/nuisance 9, 20

legal aspects, planning ex-situ
    contaminated water treatment 5-6
mercury, adsorption from groundwater
    25B
metals, biorecovery of from groundwater
    15
microbiological degradation 12-16
microfiltration 22
    EPOC microfiltration technology
        (EXXFLOW™) 25B
    membrane microfiltration 23-4B

neutralisation, using sulphuric acid or
    pure carbon dioxide 8
nonaqueous phase liquids, Ville Mercier
    33

organic compounds, aromatic and
    substitute, oxidation of 9
oxidation 9-10, 30
ozone, oxidation agent 10

packed towers 18, 33
petroleum hydrocarbons, removal by
    carbon adsorption 20
pH adjustment 8, 9, 30
phenol contamination, groundwater,
    biological treatment of 35-6
phenols, oxidation by Fenton's Reagent 9
planning permissions 5
PO*WW*ER™ Water Treatment System
    19B
powder activated carbon treatment
    (PACT™) 15, 21
precipitation 8-9, 34
    staged 9
precipitation agents, applicability of *8*
process control requirements, chemical
    treatment systems 10

reduction 10
resins, carbonaceous and polymeric, for
    selective adsorption and colour removal
    21
reverse osmosis 22, 31, 38

salt, adverse effect on biological activity
    36
sand filtration 8-9, 34
    rapid 33
sedimentation 33
slow sand filters 17
slurry bioreactors 14

soil vapour extraction with air stripping of VOCs 19B
solid residues, disposal arrangements for 10
sorption of organic compounds 21
steam cleaning, of carbon beds 21
sulphide precipitation 8

total dissolved solids (TDS), removal of 31
treatment methods 7-25
    advanced tertiary treatment techniques 22-4, 25B
    air stripping 18-20
    biological 12-16
    carbon adsorption 20-1
    chemical 8-11
    coagulation and flocculation 12
    filtration 17-18
    sorption of organic compounds 21
    summary of applicability and development status *7*
treatment trains 2-5, 28-31, *32*
    basic sequence 2
    biological/carbon sorption 28, *29*
    biophysical 29, *30*
    carbon sorption/biological 28, *29*
    designed on site-specific basis 3

heavy metals and cyanide removal 30, *31*
hexavalent chromium removal 29, *30*
important consideration in design 5
information needed to design a system 3, *4*
    additional factors 3
metals removal 29, *31*
removal of metals and ammonia, and control of total dissolved solids 31, *32*
under-designed at Ville Mercier 34

uranium, membrane microfiltration 23-4B
US Air Force, data on catalytic oxidation 19B
UV radiation/oxidation 10, *11*

Ville Mercier case 28, 32-4
volatile organic compounds (VOCs) 19B, 33

waste and wastewater treatment methods 7, *7*
Water Industry Act (1991) 5
Water Resources Act (1991) 5
water/wastewater treatment methods 2, *3*

9 Volume IX In-situ methods of remediation SP109

Volume IX describes the main process-based generic methods for the in-situ treatment of contaminated soils and groundwater. While the processes involved (thermal, physical, chemical etc.) are analogous to those used on an ex-situ basis, there are a number of important applications issues that may be more difficult to overcome. Potential constraints on in-situ applications are reviewed including the need to ensure proper control over the process, effective contact (between contaminants and treatment agents), full recovery of treatment agents, by-products and residues, and effective containment of the operation to the area being treated. The particular difficulties of demonstrating that remedial objectives have been achieved are also addressed.

Individual methods are reviewed in terms of their applicability, effectiveness, practical requirements and costs.

CONTENTS

1   **INTRODUCTION**
    1.1   Scope
    1.2   Key issues
    1.3   Legal requirements
    1.4   Site characterisation
    1.5   Applicability
    1.6   Effectiveness
    1.7   Engineering considerations
    1.8   Operational considerations
    1.9   Compliance and performance testing
    1.10   Integrating remedial methods
    References

2   **IN-SITU SOIL LEACHING AND WASHING/FLUSHING**
    2.1   Introduction
    2.2   Description of the method
    2.3   Applicability
    2.4   Planning and management
    2.5   Operational needs
    2.6   Information requirements
    2.7   Effectiveness
    2.8   Limitations
    2.9   Costs
    2.10   Prognosis
    References

3   **IN-SITU CHEMICAL TREATMENT**
    3.1   Introduction

3.2   Description of the method

3.3   Principal chemical treatment reactions

3.4   Applicability

3.5   Planning and management

3.6   Operational needs

3.7   Information requirements

3.8   Effectiveness

3.9   Limitations

3.10   Costs

3.11   Prognosis

References

4   IN-SITU BIOLOGICAL TREATMENT

4.1   Introduction

4.2   Description

4.3   Applicability

4.4   Planning and management

4.5   Operational needs

4.6   Information requirements

4.7   Effectiveness

4.8   Limitations

4.9   Costs

4.10   Prognosis

References

5   IN-SITU SOIL VAPOUR EXTRACTION

5.1   Introduction

5.2   Description

5.3   Applicability

5.4   Planning and management

5.5   Operational needs

5.6   Information requirements

5.7   Effectiveness

5.8   Limitations

5.9   Costs

5.10   Prognosis

References

6   IN-SITU THERMAL DESORPTION

6.1   Introduction

6.2   Description

6.3   Applicability

6.4   Operational needs

6.5   Information requirements

6.6   Effectiveness

6.7   Limitations

6.8   Costs

6.9   Prognosis

References

7   IN-SITU VITRIFICATION

7.1   Introduction

7.2   Description

7.3   Applicability

7.4   Planning and management

7.5   Operational needs

7.6   Information requirements

7.7   Effectiveness

7.8   Limitations

7.9   Costs

7.10   Prognosis

References

8   IN-SITU STABILISATION/SOLIDIFICATION

8.1   Introduction

8.2   Description

8.3   Applicability

8.4   Operational requirements

8.5   Information requirements

8.6   Effectiveness

8.7   Limitations

8.8   Costs

8.9   Prognosis

References

9   IN-SITU ELECTRO-REMEDIATION

9.1   Introduction

9.2   Description

9.3   Applicability

9.4   Planning and management

9.5   Operational requirements

9.6   Information requirements

9.7   Effectiveness

9.8   Limitations

9.9   Costs

9.10   Prognosis

References

10 IN-SITU GROUNDWATER REMEDIATION

10.1   Introduction

10.2   Description

10.3   Applicability

10.4   Planning and management

10.5   Operational needs

10.6   Information requirements

10.7   Effectiveness

10.8   Limitations

10.9   Costs

10.10 Prognosis

References

Appendix 1   Examples of elements and compounds belonging to different contaminant groups

Appendix 2   Principles of contaminant behaviour in the vadose zone

Appendix 3   Characteristics limiting soil vapour extraction feasibility

REFERENCES

ACAR, Y.B. and ALSHAWABKEH, A. Fundamentals of extracting species from soils by electrokinetics. *Waste Management,* 1993, **12** (3)

ACAR, Y.B. and ALSHAWABKEH, A.N. Principles of electrokinetic remediation. *Environmental Science and Technology,* 1993, **27** (13) 2638-2647

ACAR, Y.B. and HAMED, J. Electrokinetic soil processing in remediation/treatment: synthesis of available data. *Bulletin of Transportation Research,* Record No 1312, Energy and Environmental Issues 1991, pp 153-161

ACAR, Y.B. Electrokinetic soil processing: a review of the state of the art. In: *Proceedings of the ASCE Speciality Conference Ground Improvement and Grouting, New Orleans 1992.* American Society of Civil Engineers, 1992

ACAR, Y.B., GALE, R.J., PUTNAM, G. and HAMED, J. Electrochemical processing of soils: its potential use in environmental geotechnology and significance of pH gradients. In: *Proceedings of the 2nd International Symposium on Environmental Geotechnology, Shangai 1989,* Volume 1, pp 25-38

ACAR, Y.B., LI, H. and GALE, R.J. Phenol removal from kaolinite using electrokinetics. *Journal of Geotechnical Engineering,* ASCE, 1992, **118** (11)

ALLOWAY, B.J. (ed.) *Heavy Metals in Soils.* Blackie (London), 1990

ALSHAWABKEH, A. and ACAR, Y.B. Removal of contaminants from soils by electrokinetics: a theoretical treatise. *Journal Environmental Science and Health,* 1992, **27**(7), 1835-1861

ANDERSON, T.A. *et al.* Bioremediation in the rhizosphere: plant roots and associated microbes clean contaminated soils. *Environmental Science and Technology.* 1993, **27** (13) 2630-2636

ANDERSON, W.C. (ed.) *Innovative site remediation technology: bioremediation.* American Association of Environmental Engineers (Annapolis), 1994

ANDERSON, W.C. (ed.) *Innovative site remediation technology: soil washing/ soil flushing.* American Academy of Environmental Engineers (Annapolis), 1993

ANDERSON, W.C. (ed.) *Innovative site remediation technology: vacuum vapor extraction.* American Academy of Environmental Engineers (Annapolis), 1994

ANDERSON, W.C. *Innovative site remediation technology: chemical treatment,* American Association of Environmental Engineers (Annapolis), 1994

ANON. Canada evaluates in situ bioremediation in ground water. *Ground Water Currents,* 1993 (March), 3-4, EPA/542/N-93/003

ANON. Fungal field-trials clean-up PCDs. *HAZNEWS,* 1990, (25), 14

ANON. Soil treatment by vacuum extraction at Verona Well Field. In: *Proceedings of the 1st International NATO/CCMS Conference on Demonstration of Remedial Action Technologies for Contaminated Land and Groundwater,* Bilthoven 1988. US Environmental Protection Agency (Cincinnati), 1988, pp 217-240

ARMISHAW, R. *et al. Review of Innovative Contaminated Soil Clean-up Processes*, Warren Spring Laboratory (Stevenage), 1992

ARMISHAW, R., BARDOS, R.P., DUNN, R.M., HILL, J.M., PEARL, M., RAMPLING, T., and WOOD, P.A. *Review of innovative contaminated soil clean-up processes*. LR 819 (MR). Warren Spring Laboratory (Stevenage), 1992

BARR, D.P. and AUST, S.D. Mechanisms white rot fungi use to degrade pollutants. *Environmental Science and Technology*, 1994, **28** (2), 78A-87A

BARRY, D.L. *Treatment options for contaminated land*. Report for Department of the Environment. Atkins Research & Development (Epsom), 1982

BELL, R. M. *Higher Plant Accumulation of Organic Pollutants from Soil Final Report under Cooperative Agreement, CR 812845-01*. US Environmental Protection Agency (Cincinnati), 1988

BRADSHAW, A. D. and CHADWICK, M. J. *The Restoration of Land*. Blackwell (London), 1980

BREEZE, V.G. *Agric. Res.* 1973, **12**, 71-81

BREEZE, V.G. *Journ. Applied Ecology*, 1973, **10** (2), 513-525

BRUELL, C.J., SEGALL, B.A. and WALSH, M.T. Electro-osmotic removal of gasoline hydrocarbons and TCE from clay. *Journal of Environmental Engineering, ASCE.*, 1991

BUERMANN, W. In-situ groundwater remediation of strippable contaminants with under-pressure-vaporizer-wells (UVB): results of numerical calculations. In: *Contaminated Soil '90*, Arendt, F., Hinsenveld, M., van den Brink, W.J. (eds.). Kluwer (Dordrecht), 1990, pp 1065-1066

BUERMANN, W. Investigation on the circulation flow around the combined withdrawal and infiltration well for groundwater remediation – demonstrated for the under-pressure vaporizer well. In: *Contaminated Soil '90*, Arendt, F., Hinsenveld, M., van den Brink, W.J. (eds.). Kluwer (Dordrecht), 1990, pp 1045-1052

CAIRNEY, T. (ed.). *Contaminated Land: Problems and Solutions*. Blackie Academic and Professional (Glasgow), 1993

CASEGRANDE, L. *The application of electro-osmosis to practical problems in foundations and earthworks*. Building Technical Paper No. 30. HMSO (London), 1947

CHEVRON RESEARCH AND TECHNOLOGY COMPANY. *Vapor Extraction System Performance Study*. CRTC internal document

CLARKE, A.N., PLUMB, P.D., SUBRAMANYAN, and WILSON, D.J. Soil clean-up by surfactant washing: I. Laboratory results and mathematical modeling. *Separation Science and Technology*, 1991, **25** (3), 301-343

CLINE, P.V. *et al.* Partitioning of aromatic constituents into water from gasoline and other complex solvent mixtures. *Environmental Science and Technology*, 1991, **26** (5), 914-920

COFFA, S., URLINGS, L. G.C.M., and VIJGEN, J.M.H. Soil vapour extraction of hydrocarbons in situ and on site biological treatment at a gasoline station. In: *Demonstration of Remedial Action Technologies for Contaminated Land and Groundwater, Final Report, Volume 2 – Part 2*. EPA/600/R-93/012c. US Environmental Protection Agency (Cincinnati), 1993, pp 1018-1029

COSTA, M. J. Remediating contaminated aquifers: a reality with two-phase vacuum extraction. In: *Proceedings of the HMC/SUPERFUND '92 Conference, Washington DC, 1992*. Hazardous Materials Control Resources Institute (Greenbelt, Maryland), 1992, pp 886-889

CROWHURST, D., and MANCHESTER, S.J. *The measurement of methane and other gases from the ground*. Special Report 131. CIRIA (London), 1993

de BRUIJN, P. and VERHEUL, J.H.A.M. Biotreatment in soil remediation. In: *Proceedings of a Conference on Contaminated Land: Policy, Regulation and Technology, London 1992*. IBC Technical Services (London), 1992

Demonstration of Remedial Action Technologies for Contaminated Land and Groundwater. EPA/600/R-93/012. US Environmental Protection Agency, Risk Reduction Engineering Laboratory (Cincinnati), 1993

DICKINSON, W., DICKINSON, R.W., MOTE, P.A. and NELSON, J.S. Horizontal radials for geophysics and hazardous waste remediation. In: *Proceedings of the 8th National Conference, Superfund '87*, pp 371-375. Hazardous Materials Control Research Institute (Silver Spring), 1987

DOWNEY, D. C., HINCHEE, R. E., WESTRAY, M. S. and SLAUGHTER, J. K. Combined biological and physical treatment of a jet fuel-contaminated aquifer. In: *Demonstration of Remedial Action Technologies for Contaminated Land and Groundwater, Volume 2, Part 2*, EPA/600/R-93/012c. US Environmental Protection Agency, Risk Reduction Engineering Laboratory (Cincinnati), 1993, pp 1329-1347

DRINKARD, W.F. *Electrochemical mining of copper*. 1976, US Patent 3956007

ELLIS, W.D., PAYNE, J.R., and McNABB, G.D. *Treatment of contaminated soils with aqueous surfactants*. EPA/600/2-85/129. US Environmental Protection Agency (Cincinnati), 1985

FLEMING, G. (ed.) *Recycling Derelict Land*. Thomas Telford (London), 1991

FOUNTAIN, J.C. Surfactant flushing of ground water removes DNAPLs. EPA/542/N-92/006. *Ground Water Currents*, 1992 (December), 1, 3 & 4

GEMMELL, R.P. *Environ. Pollut.* 1973, **5**, 181-197

GEMMELL, R.P. *Environ. Pollut.* 1974, **6**, 31-37

GEMMELL, R.P. *In: Ecology of Resource Degradation and Renewals*. Chadwick, M. J. and Goodman, G. T. (eds.) Blackwell Scientific Publications (London), 1975, pp385-403

GEMMELL, R.P. *Nature*, 1972, **240**, 569-571

GEMMELL, R.P. *Surveyor*, 1973 (2 Nov) 36-38

GEOSAFE. *Application and Evaluation Considerations for In-situ vitrification Technology: A Treatment Process for destruction and/or Permanent Immobilisation of Hazardous Materials.* GSC 1901. Geosafe Corporation (Kirkland WA), 1989

GRAY, D.H. and MITCHELL, J.K. Fundamental aspects of electro-osmosis in soils *ASCE (SM)* 1967, **93** (9) 209-236

GUERRIERO, M.M. In-situ vacuum extraction Verona Well Field Superfund Site, Battle Creek, Michigan. In: *Demonstration of Remedial Action Technologies for Contaminated Land and Groundwater, Final Report, Volume 2 – Part 2.* EPA/600/R-93/012c. US Environmental Protection Agency (Cincinnati), 1993, pp 1032-1052

HAMED, J., GALE, R.J. and ACAR, Y.B. Pb(II) removal from kaolinite using electrokinetics. *Journal of Geotechnical Engineering,* ASCE, 1991, **112** (February) 241-271

HANSEN, J. and FITZPATRICK, V. In-situ vitrification: heat and immobilisation are combined for soil remediation. *Hazmat World,* 1989 (December)

HANSEN, J.E. and FITZPATRICK, V.F. In-situ vitrification applications. In: *Proceedings of the 3rd Forum on Innovative Hazardous Waste Treatment Technologies: Domestic and International, 1991.* US Environmental Protection Agency (Washington DC), 1991

HANSEN, J. *Status of In situ Vitrification Technology: A Treatment Process for Destruction and/or Permanent Immobilisation.* Geosafe Corporation (Kirkland WA)

HERRLING, B. and STAMM, J. Vertical circulation systems for in situ bioreclamation and in situ remediation of strippable contaminants. In: *Proceedings of an International Symposium on Soil Decontamination Using Biological processes* (Karlsruhe), 1992

HERRLING, B., STAMM, J., BOTT-BREUNING, G. and DIEKMAN, S. In situ bioremediation of groundwater containing hydrocarbons, pesticides, or nitrate using vertical circulation flows (UVB/GZB technique) In: *In Situ and On-Site Bioreclamation: Second International Symposium Proceedings,* R.E. Hinchee (ed.) Butterworth-Heinemann (Boston), 1993

HICKS, R.E. and TONDORF, G. Electro-restoration of metal contaminated soils. *Enviromental Science and Technology,* 1994, **28**, 2203-2210

HINCHEE, R.E., ONG, S.K., MILLER, R.N., DOWNEY, D.C., and FRANDT, R. *Test Plan and Technical Protocol for a Field Treatability Test for Bioventing.* US Air Force, Center for Environmental Excellence (Brooks Air Force Base, Texas), 1992

HINSENVELD, M. Physical/chemical extraction technologies. In: *Demonstration of Remedial Action Technologies for Contaminated Land and Groundwater, Final Report, Volume 1.* EPA/600/R-93/012a. USEPA (Cincinnati), 1993, pp 53-63

JOHNSON, P.C., KEMBLOWSKI, M.W. and COLTHART, J.D. Quantitative analysis for the cleanup of hydrocarbon contaminated soils by in situ soil venting. *Ground Water,* 1990, **28** (3), 413

JOHNSON, P.C., STANLEY, C.C., KEMBLOWSKI, M.W., BYERS, D.L. and COLTHART, J.D. A practical approach to the design, operation, and monitoring of in situ soil-venting systems. *Ground Water Monitoring Review,* 1990, pp 159-178

KARLSSON, K. and BITTO, R. New horizontal wellbore system for monitor and remedial wells. In: *Proceedings of the 11th National Conference, Superfund '90.* Hazardous Materials Control Research Institute (Silver Spring, MD), 1990, pp 357-362

KING, J., TINTO, T., and RIDOSH, M. In situ treatment of pesticide contaminated soils. In: *Proceedings of the 6th National Conference on the Management of Uncontrolled Hazardous Waste Sites.* Hazardous Materials Control Research Institute (Silver Spring, Maryland), 1985, pp 243-248

LAGEMAN, R. Electroremediation Applications in the Netherlands. *Environmental Science and Technology,* 2648-2650

LAGEMAN, R., POOL, W. and SEFFINGA, G.A. Electro-reclamation: theory and practice. *Chemistry & Industry,* 1989 (18 Sept), 585-590

LAGEMAN, R., WIEBEREN, P. and SEFFINGA, G.A. Electro-reclamation: state-of-the-art. In: *Proceedings of the 4th Annual Conference on Contaminated Land: Policy, Economics and Technology, London 1993.* IBC Technical Services Ltd (London), 1993

LEACH, B.A. and GOODGER, H.K. *Building on Derelict Land.* Special Publication 78. CIRIA (London), 1991

LEWIS, N. Soil vapor extraction technologies. In: *Demonstration of remedial action technologies for contaminated land and groundwater, Final Report, Vol. 1.* EPA/600/R-93/012a. US Environmental Protection Agency (Cincinnati), 1993, pp 33-52

LICENCE, G. In situ remediation using vacuum extraction techniques. In: *Remedial Processes for Contaminated Land,* M. Pratt (edit). Institution of Chemical Engineers (Rugby), 1993, pp 113-119

LINDGREN, E.R., MATTSON, E.D. and KOZAK, M.W. Electrokinetic remediation of anionic contaminants from unsaturated soils. In: *Proceedings of an International Symposium on Environmental Contamination in Central and Eastern Europe, Budapest 1992.* Technical University of Budapest/Florida State University, 1992, pp 614-618

LOO, W.W. and WANG, I. Remediation of groundwater aquifer by in situ electrolysis and electro-osmosis. In: *Proceedings of the National Research & Development Conference on the Control of Hazardous Materials, Anaheim 1991.* HMCRI (Greenbelt, Maryland), 1991, pp 163-165

MACDONALD, J.A. and RITTMANN, B.E. Performance standards for in situ bioremediation. *Environmental Science and Technology,* 1993, **27** (10), 1974-1979

MATTHESS, G. In-situ treatment of arsenic contaminated groundwater. In: *Proceedings of an International Symposium on Quality of Groundwater, Noordwijkerhout 1981,* in: Gasberger (ed.), Studies in Environmental Science, Vol 17

McGRATH, S.P., SIDOULI, C.M.D., BAKER, A.J.M. and REEVES, R.D. The potential for the use of metal-accumulating plants for the in situ decontamination of metal-polluted sites. In: *Proceedings of the International Conference 'Eurosol', Maastricht,* 1992

MILES, J., LATTER, P.M., SMITH, I.R. and HEAL, O.W. Ecological effects of killing *Bacillus anthracis* on Gruinard Island with formaldehyde. *Reclamation and Revegetation Research,* 1988 **6**, 271-283

MILLER, R.N., HINCHEE, R.E., VOGEL, C.M., DUPONT, R.R. and DOWNEY, D. C. A field investigation of enhanced hydrocarbon biodegradation in the vadose zone at Tyndall AFB, Florida. In: *Demonstration of Remedial Action Technologies for Contaminated Land and Groundwater, Volume 2, Part 2.* EPA/600/R-93/012c. US Environmental Protection Agency, Risk Reduction Engineering Laboratory (Cincinnati), 1993, pp 1054-1066

MINISTRY OF AGRICULTURE FISHERIES AND FOOD. *Lime and Liming.* MAFF Bulletin 35. HMSO (London), 1973

MURDOCH, L., PATTERSON, B., LOSONSKY, G., and HARRAR, W. *Innovative Technologies for Delivery or Recovery: A Review of Current Research and a Strategy for Maximising Future Investigations.* Report for Contract No. 68-03-3379. US Environmental Protection Agency (Cincinnati), 1988

NANNIPIERI, P. and BOLLAG, J.M. Use of enzymes to detoxify pesticide-contaminated soils and water. *Journal of Environmental Quality,* 1991, **20** (3), 510-517

NATIONAL RESEARCH COUNCIL. *Alternatives for groundwater cleanup.* National Academy Press (Washington DC), 1994

NATIONAL RESEARCH COUNCIL. *In situ bioremediation: When does it work?* National Academy Press (Washington DC), 1993

NELSON, C.H., HICKS, R.J. and ANDREWS, S.D. In situ bioremediation: an integrated approach. In: *Proceedings of HMC/SUPERFUND '92, Washington DC, 1992.* Hazardous Materials Control Resources Institute (Greenbelt, Maryland), 1992, pp 416-429

O'HANNESIN, S.F. and GILHAM, R.W. In situ degradation of halogenated organics by permeable reaction wall. *Ground Water Currents,* 1993 (March), 1-2, EPA/542/N-93/003

PARK, J.E. *Testing and evaluation of permeable materials for removing pollutants from leachates at remedial action sites.* EPA/600/2-86/074. US Environmental Protection Agency, 1986

PINIEWSKI, R. OBERLS, D. and BOERSMAN, P. Vacuum extraction/groundwater sparging system for in situ remediation of soil and groundwater. In: *Proceedings of the HMC/SUPERFUND '92 conference, Washington DC, 1992.* Hazardous Materials Control Resources Institute (Greenbelt, Maryland), 1992, pp 870-878

PLAINES, A.L., PINIESKI, R.J. and YARBROUGH, G.D. Integrated vacuum extraction/pneumatic soil fracturing system for remediation of low permeability soils. In: *Proceedings of the HMC/SUPERFUND '92 Conference, Washington DC, 1992.* Hazardous Materials Control Resources Institute (Greenbelt, Maryland), 1992, pp 637-642

POOL, W. HYDRACONSULT BV. *A process for the electroremediation of soil material, an electric current system for application of the process, and an electrode housing for use in the electric current system.* 1992, European Patent 0 312 174 B1 (application made in 1988)

PROBSTEIN, R.F. Electro-osmotic purging for in situ remediation. In: *Demonstration of Remedial Action Technologies for Contaminated Land and Groundwater, Final Report, Volume 2, Part 1.* EPA/600/R-93/012b. US Environmental Protection Agency (Cincinnati), 1993, pp 603-634

PUGHOLM, K. Cyanide-contaminated soil purified in-situ. *Pollution Prevention,* 1993, **3** (1), 35-36

PURI, A.N. Reclamation of alkali soils by electrodialysis. *Soil Science,* 1949, **42,** 23-27

RISS, A. and RIPPER, P. Soil and groundwater sanitation on the area of the waste-oil refinery Pintsch-Öl, Hanau: Large scale tests and biorestoration. In: *Contaminated Soil '90,* Arendt, F., Hinsenveld, M., van den Brink, W.J. (eds.). Kluwer Academic Publishers (Dordrecht), 1990, pp 1033-1034

ROUSE, J.D. and SABATINI, D.A. Minimising surfactant losses using twin-head anionic surfactants in subsurface remediation. *Environmental Science and Technology,* 1993, **27** (10), 2072-2076

SANNING, D.E. In-situ treatment. In: *Contaminated Land: Reclamation and Treatment,* M.A. Smith (ed.). Plenum (London), 1985, pp 91-111

SCALF, M. Biological cleanup of TCE, DCE, and VC in ground water. *Tech Trends,* 1990, (1), 1 & 3, EPA/540/M-90/008

SHAPIRO, A.P., RENAULD, P. and PROBSTEIN, R. Preliminary studies on removal of chemical species from saturated porous media by electro-osmosis. *Physicochemical Hydrodynamics,* 1989, **11** (5/6), 785-802

SIKES, D.J., McCULLOUGH, M.N. and BLACKBURN, J.W. The containment and mitigation of a formaldehyde rail car spill using novel chemical and biological in-situ treatment techniques. In: *Proceedings of a Hazardous Materials Spill Conference: Prevention, Behavior, Control and Cleanup of Spills and Waste sites.* Nashville, 1984, pp 98-103

SMITH, M.A. (ed.) *Contaminated Land: Reclamation and Treatment.* Plenum Press (New York), 1985

STAPS, S.J.J.M. *International Evaluation of In-situ Biorestoration of Contaminated Soil and Groundwater.* EPA/540/2-90/012. US Environmental Protection Agency (Washington DC), 1990

STAPS, S. Microbial treatment technologies. In: *Demonstration of Remedial Action Technologies for Contaminated Land and Groundwater, Volume 1.* EPA/600/R-93/012a. US Environmental Protection Agency, Risk Reduction Engineering Laboratory (Cincinnati), 1993, pp 85-95

STARR, R.C. and CHERRY, J.C. Funnel and gate system directs plumes to in situ treatment. *Ground Water Currents,* 1993 (June) 1 & 4, EPA/542/N-93/006

STEED, J.E., SHEPHERD, E., and BARRY, D.L. *A guide to safe working practices for contaminated sites.* Report 132. CIRIA (London), 1966

STURGES, S.G., McBETH, P. and PRATT, C.P. Performance of soil flushing and groundwater extraction at the United Chrome Superfund site. *Journal of Hazardous Materials*, 1992, **29**, 59-78

SVOMA, J. In situ treatment of groundwater polluted with chlorinated hydrocarbons In: *Contaminated Soil '90*, Arendt, F., Hinsenveld, M., van den Brink, W.J. (eds.). Kluwer (Dordrecht), 1990, pp 1143-1144

TANAKA, J.C. Soil vapour extraction system: Verona Well Field Superfund Site, Battle creek, Michigan USA. In: *Proceedings of the 1st International NATO/CCMS Conference on Demonstration of Remedial Action Technologies for Contaminated Land and Groundwater, Washington DC 1987*. US Environmental Protection Agency (Cincinnati), 1987, pp 182-187

TEELON, C. Horizontal wells for cost effective in situ air stripping. *Tech Trends*, 1992, (8), 1 & 2, EPA/542/N-92/001

THEILE, P. Vacuum extraction technology for the treatment of sub-surface pollution: a case study. In: *Proceedings of a Conference on Contaminated Land: Policy, Regulation and Technology, London 1992*. IBC Technical Services (London), 1992

TOPP, E., SCHEUNERT, I., ATTAR, A. and KORTE, F. Factors affecting the uptake of 14C-labelled organic compounds by plants from soil. *Ecotoxicology and Environmental Safety*, 1986, **11**, 219-228

TRAVIS, C.C., and MACINNIS, J.M. *Environmental Science and Technology*, 1992, **10**(10), 1885-1887

TRAVIS, C.C., and MACINNIS, J.M. Vapour extraction of organics from the subsurface soils: is it effective? *Environmental Science and Technology*, 1992, **26** (10), 1885-1887

TROWBRIDGE, B.E. and OTT, D.E. The use of in situ dual vacuum extraction for remediation of soil and groundwater. In: *Proceedings of the HMC/SUPERFUND '92 Conference, Washington DC, 1992*. Hazardous Materials Control Resources Institute (Greenbelt, Maryland), 1992, pp 643-647

URLINGS, L.G.C.M., ACKERMANN, V.P., VAN WOUDENBERG, J.C., VAN DEN PILJ, P.P., and GAASTRA, J.J. In-situ cadmium removal. In: *Demonstration of Remedial Action Technologies for Contaminated Land and Groundwater, Volume 2 – Part 2*. EPA/600/R-93/012c. US Environmental Protection Agency (Cincinnati) 1993, pp 1135-1156

US ENVIRONMENTAL PROTECTION AGENCY. ABB Environmental Services, Inc: Two zone interception in situ treatment strategy. In: *The Superfund Innovative Technology Evaluation Program: Technology Profiles*. Seventh Edition, EPA/540/R-94/526. US EPA (Washington DC), 1994, pp 316-317

US ENVIRONMENTAL PROTECTION AGENCY. ABB Environmental Services, Inc: Two-zone interception in situ treatment strategy. In: *The Superfund Innovative Technology Evaluation Program: Technology Profiles*, Sixth Edition, EPA/540/R-93/526. USEPA (Washington DC), 1993, pp 276-277

US ENVIRONMENTAL PROTECTION AGENCY. *Applications Analysis Report: Accutech pneumatic fracturing extraction and hot gas injection, Phase 1.* EPA/540/AR-93/509. USEPA (Washington DC), 1993

US ENVIRONMENTAL PROTECTION AGENCY. *Applications Analysis Report: Terra Vac In Situ Vacuum Extraction System.* EPA/540/A-5/003. USEPA (Cincinnati), 1989

US ENVIRONMENTAL PROTECTION AGENCY. *Applications Analysis Report: Toxic Treatments, In situ steam/hot-air stripping technology.* EPA/540/A5-90/008. USEPA Office of Research and Development (Washington DC), 1991

US ENVIRONMENTAL PROTECTION AGENCY. *Assessing UST Correction Action Technologies: Site assessment and selection of unsaturated zone treatment technologies.* EPA/600/2-90/011. USEPA (Washington DC), 1990

US ENVIRONMENTAL PROTECTION AGENCY. *Basics of pump-and-treat ground-water remediation technology.* EPA/600/8-90/003. USEPA Robert S Kerr Environmental Research Laboratory (Ada, OK), 1990

US ENVIRONMENTAL PROTECTION AGENCY. *Decision-Support Software for Soil Vapor Extraction, Technology Application: Hyperventilate.* Manual, EPA/600/R-93/028. USEPA (Washington DC), 1993

US ENVIRONMENTAL PROTECTION AGENCY. *Decision-Support Software for Soil Vapor Extraction, Technology Application: Hyperventilate.* Diskettes. USEPA (Washington DC), 1993

US ENVIRONMENTAL PROTECTION AGENCY. *Engineering Bulletin: In situ steam extraction treatment.* EPA/540/2-91/005. USEPA (Cincinnati), 1991

US ENVIRONMENTAL PROTECTION AGENCY. *Engineering Bulletin: In situ soil vapor extraction treatment.* EPA/540/2-91/006. USEPA (Washington DC), 1991

US ENVIRONMENTAL PROTECTION AGENCY. Geochem (A division of Terra Vac): In situ remediation of chromium in groundwater. In: *The Superfund Innovative Technology Evaluation Program: Technology Profiles.* Sixth Edition, EPA/540/R-93/526. USEPA (Washington DC), 1993, pp 154-155

US ENVIRONMENTAL PROTECTION AGENCY. Geosafe Corporation (In-situ vitrification). In: *The Superfund Innovative Technology Evaluation Program: Technology Profiles.* Fifth Edition, EPA/540/R-92/077. USEPA (Cincinnati), 1992, pp 96-97

US ENVIRONMENTAL PROTECTION AGENCY. *Handbook on the in situ treatment of hazardous waste-contaminated soil.* EPA/540/2-90/002. USEPA (Cincinnati), 1990

US ENVIRONMENTAL PROTECTION AGENCY. *Handbook: Ground water: Volume I. Ground water and contamination.* EPA/625/6-90/16a. Office of Research and Development, USEPA (Washington DC), 1990

US ENVIRONMENTAL PROTECTION AGENCY. *Handbook: Vitrification technologies for the treatment of hazardous and radioactive wastes.* EPA/625/R-92/002. USEPA Office of Research and Development (Washington DC), 1992

US ENVIRONMENTAL PROTECTION AGENCY. Hazardous Waste Control: Nomix(r) Technology. In: *The Superfund Innovative Technology Evaluation Program: Technology Profiles*, Fifth Edition, EPA/540/R-92/077. USEPA (Washington DC), 1992, pp 100-101

US ENVIRONMENTAL PROTECTION AGENCY. Hrubetz Environmental Services, Inc: HRUBOUTR Process. In: *The Superfund Innovative Technology Evaluation Program: Technology Profiles*. Fifth Edition, EPA/540/R-93/526. USEPA (Washington DC), 1993, pp 72-73

US ENVIRONMENTAL PROTECTION AGENCY. Hughes Environmental Systems, Inc: Steam enhanced recovery process. In: *The Superfund Innovative Technology Evaluation Program: Technology Profiles*. Sixth Edition, EPA/540/R-93/526. USEPA (Washington DC), 1992, pp 74-75

US ENVIRONMENTAL PROTECTION AGENCY. Illinois Institute of Technology Research Institute/ Halliburton NUS: Radio frequency heating. In: *The Superfund Innovative Technology Evaluation Program: Technology Profiles*. Sixth edition, EPA/540/R-93/526. USEPA (Washington DC), 1993, pp 76-77

US ENVIRONMENTAL PROTECTION AGENCY. *In Situ Treatment of Contaminated Ground Water: An inventory of Research and Field Demonstrations and Strategies for Improving Ground Water Remediation*. USEPA (Washington DC), 1993

US ENVIRONMENTAL PROTECTION AGENCY. *Innovative Treatment Technologies, Overview and Guide to Information Sources*. EPA/540/9-91/002. USEPA Office of Solid Waste and Emergency Response (Washington DC), 1991

US ENVIRONMENTAL PROTECTION AGENCY. *International Waste Technologies/Geo-Con in situ stabilization/solidification*. Applications Analysis Report, EPA/540/A5-89/004. USEPA (Cincinnati), 1990

US ENVIRONMENTAL PROTECTION AGENCY. IT Corporation: Photolytic and biological soil detoxification. In: *The Superfund Innovative Technology Evaluation Program: Technology Profiles*. Sixth edition, EPA/540/R-93/526. USEPA (Washington DC), 1993, pp 248-249

US ENVIRONMENTAL PROTECTION AGENCY. *Project summary: In-situ aquifer restoration of chlorinated aliphatics by methanotrophic bacteria*. EPA/600/S2-89/033. USEPA Robert S Kerr Environmental Research Laboratory (Ada, OK), 1989

US ENVIRONMENTAL PROTECTION AGENCY. S.M.W. Seiko Inc: In situ solidification and stabilization. In: *The Superfund Innovative Technology Evaluation Program: Technology Profiles*. Sixth edition, EPA/540/R-93/526. USEPA (Washington DC), 1993, pp 184-185

US ENVIRONMENTAL PROTECTION AGENCY. *Seminar Publication: transport and fate of contaminants in the subsurface*. EPA/625/4-80/019. US Environmental Protection Agency (Cincinnati), 1989

US ENVIRONMENTAL PROTECTION AGENCY. *SITE Demonstration Bulletin: Radio-frequency heating: IIT Research Institute*. EPA/540/MR-94/527. USEPA (Cincinnati), 1994

US ENVIRONMENTAL PROTECTION AGENCY. *SITE Demonstration Bulletin: Radio-frequency heating: KAI Technologies Inc.* EPA/540/MR-94/527. USEPA (Cincinnati), 1994

US ENVIRONMENTAL PROTECTION AGENCY. *SITE Technology Capsule: Geosafe Corporation in-situ vitrification technology.* EPA/540/R-94/520a. USEPA Office of Research and Development (Cincinnati), 1994

US ENVIRONMENTAL PROTECTION AGENCY. *Soil Vapour Extraction Technology Reference Handbook.* EPA/540/2-91/011. USEPA, 1991

US ENVIRONMENTAL PROTECTION AGENCY. *Technology Demonstration Summary: Hydraulic fracturing technology.* EPA/540/SR-93/505. USEPA (Cincinnati), 1993

US ENVIRONMENTAL PROTECTION AGENCY. *The Superfund Innovative Technology Evaluation Program: Technology Profiles.* Seventh edition, EPA/540/R-94/526. USEPA (Washington DC), 1994

US ENVIRONMENTAL PROTECTION AGENCY. Udell Technologies Inc., In situ steam enhanced extraction. In: *The Superfund Innovative Technology Evaluation Program: Technology Profiles.* Sixth edition, EPA/540/R-93/526. USEPA (Washington DC), 1993, pp 196-197

US ENVIRONMENTAL PROTECTION AGENCY. Western Research Institute: Contained recovery of oily wastes. In: *The Superfund Innovative Technology Evaluation Program: Technology Profiles.* Sixth edition, EPA/540/R-93/526. USEPA (Washington DC), 1993., pp 198-199

VADYUMINA, A.F. Improvement of saline soils by electrical treatment *Vestn. Mosk. Univ. Serv. VI,* 1966, **21**(4) 89-100

van VREE, H.B.R.J., URLINGS, L.G.C.M. and GELDNER, P. In situ biorestoration of soil contaminated with aromatic, polyaromatic and phenolic compounds. In: *Contaminated Soil '90,* F. Arendt, M. Hinsenveld, W.J. van den Brink (eds). Kluwer Academic Publishers (Dordrecht), 1990, pp 1019-1120

VOGEL, C. Bioventing of hydrocarbon contaminated soils in sub-arctic conditions. In: *Proceedings of the First International Conference, NATO/CCMS Pilot Study, Evaluation of Demonstrated and Emerging Technologies for the Treatment and Clean-up of Contaminated Land and Groundwater (Phase II),* Québec, 1993

WAGNER, K., BOYER, K., CLAFF, R., EVANS, M., HENRY, S., HODGE, V., MAHMUD, S., SARNO, D., SCOPINA, E., and SPOONER, P. *Remedial action technology for waste disposal sites* (2nd edition). Noyes Data Corporation (Park Ridge, New Jersey), 1986

WEST, C.T. and HARWELL, J.H. Surfactants and subsurface remediation. *Environmental Science and Technology,* 1992, **26** (12), 2324-2330

WILLIAMS, E.B. Contaminant containment by in situ polymerization. In: *Proceedings of the 2nd National Conference Restoration and Ground-water Monitoring.* National Water Wells Association (USA), 1982

INDEX

Note: Numbers in italics refer to Tables. B indicates a Box, and Ap indicates an Appendix

ABB Environmental Services,
  biodegradation of chlorinated
  hydrocarbons 148B
advection-limited sites 91B
Air Quality Regulations (1989) 7
air-sparging for groundwater remediation
  76, 76B, 149, *156*
  with bioventing 56, *57*
air-stripping and groundwater circulation
  wells, groundwater remediation 150-1,
  156
aircraft plant contamination,
  bioremediation for 55B
alkali polyethylene glycolate (APEG)
  process
    dechlorination of PCBs 39B, *41*
    environmental impact 44B
Alternative Treatment Technology Centre
  (ATTIC) database 5
American Academy of Environmental
  Engineers (AAEE) 5
anthrax disinfection 40, 42B
applicability matrix of in-situ treatments
  8, *9*
Application Analysis Reports (USEPA) 5
asphalt manufacturing site,
  bioremediation for 55B

biodegradation of chlorinated
  hydrocarbons, groundwater remediation
  148B
biological treatment/remediation, in-situ
  applicability *9*, 61, *62*
  at depth examples 55B
  by composting soils 50B
  cell-free enzymes 60, *62*
  costs 69-1
  effectiveness 68
  environmental impacts 63-4
  evaluation of projects 66, *67*
  health and safety 64
  information requirements 64-5, 65B
  integrated 58B, *59*
  laboratory support 64
  PCB bearing soils 50B
  planning and management 61-2
  plant and equipment 63
  principle 49
  prognosis 70
  quality management 64

site requirements 63
technical specifications 62-3
treatability studies 65-6
vegetation uptake 57-60
white rot fungi 60, 61B
  see also microbial treatment,
    bioventing
bioventing
  with air-sparging 56
  Hill Air Force Base, Utah 56B
  microbial treatment 53, *54*, 55B
  with soil vapour extraction 53, *57*, 76B
  with water filtration 53
  with/without extraction *54*

cadmium, in-situ flushing case study
  26B, *27*
carbon adsorption, with soil vapour
  extraction 75
carbon dioxide flushing 20B
carbon dioxide injection *10*
catalytic converters, with SVE 75
cell-free enzymes, biological treatment
  60, *62*
chemical treatment, in-situ
  applications 31-2, 40, *41*
  availability reduction 32-3
  costs 47
  dechlorination 39
  degrading contaminants with surface
    treatment 31-2
  effectiveness 46
  environmental protection 43, 44B
  health and safety 45
  information requirements 45, *45*
  laboratory support 44
  limitations *46*
  planning and management 40-3
  plant and equipment 43
  principle 31
  prognosis 47
  quality management 44-5
  site requirements 43
  with soil flushing 32
  surface soils 44B
  see also oxidation; polymerisation;
    reduction
chlorinated hydrocarbons,
  biodegraduation of, groundwater
  remediation, in-situ 148B

chromium contamination
   groundwater remediation 146B
   soil flushing and groundwater
      extraction 28B
   use of ferrous sulphate 32
chromium, hexavalent, reduction of 37-8,
   38B
classification system for treatment 1, 2
co-metabolism, microbial treatment 51,
   62
colloidal gas aphrons, microbial
   treatment 51, 62
compliance testing 14-15
containment, for soil flushing systems 19
contaminant composition 171Ap
contaminant identification 7
Control of Substances Hazardous to
   Health (COSHH) Regulations 85
corrosives, elements and compounds of
   165Ap, 166Ap
costs
   biological treatment 69-1
   chemical treatment 47
   electro-remediation, in-situ 139
   groundwater remediation, in-situ 161
   leaching/washing/flushing 29
   soil vapour extraction (SVE) 96
   stabilisation/solidification, in-situ 130-
      1
   thermal desorption 107
   vitrification, in-situ (ISV) 119
Croal valley, Bolton, reduction of
   hexavalent chromium 38B
cyanides, elements and compounds of
   165Ap
cyclic pumping 10

Darcy's law 172Ap
dechlorination
   environmental impact 44B
   information requirements 45B
   limitations 46
   for PCBs 39B, 41
   reactions 39
deep soil mixing (DSM) techniques 124,
   125
delivery systems 12-13
   applicability 13
dense non-aqueous phase liquids
   (DNAPLs) 150-1, 155
desorption see thermal desorption
diffusion-limited sites 91B
dioxins/furans, elements and compounds
   of 165Ap
disinfection

applicability 9, 41
   Gruinard Island, anthrax spores 40,
     42B
dorn effect/settling potential 133B
dual vacuum extraction 77B
Duty of Care, Health and Safety at Work
   Act (1974) 6, 7

electro-osmosis 132, 133B
electro-remediation, in-situ
   applicability 9, 135
   costs 139
   effectiveness 138-9
   energy requirements 135
   environmental protection 137
   equipment 137
   field application 133-4
   health and safety 137
   information requirements 138
   laboratory support 137
   limitations 139
   monitoring 137
   planning and management 136
   procurement 136
   prognosis 140
   scientific basis 132
   site requirements 137
   specification 136, 136B
   treatment duration 134
electrokinetics 10, 133B, 134
electrolysis 132, 133B
electromigration 132, 133B
electrophoresis 132, 133B
Engineering Bulletins (USEPA) 5
engineering considerations 12
enhanced volatisation, applicability 9
environmental impacts, biological
   treatment 63-4
environmental protection
   electro-remediation, in-situ 137
   groundwater remediation, in-situ 157
   leaching/washing/flushing 22-3
   regulations and consents 6-7
   soil vapour extraction (SVE) 84
   stabilisation/solidification, in-situ 127
   thermal desorption 105
   vitrification, in-situ (ISV) 116
Environmental Protection Act (EPA)
   (1990) 6, 7, 97

flushing see leaching/washing/flushing
formaldehyde spill, bioremediation for
   55B

genetically engineered microbes,

microbial treatment *51*
groundwater circulation well,
    groundwater remediation 150
groundwater extraction, with soil vapour
    extraction (SVE) 76B
groundwater remediation, in-situ
    air-sparging 149
    air-stripping and groundwater
        circulation wells 150-1
    applicability 155-6, *156*
    biodegraduation of chlorinated
        hydrocarbons 148B
    chlorinated solvents, removal with
        horizontal wells 149B
    chromium treatments 146B
    costs 161
    effectiveness 160
    environmental protection 157
    funnel and gate systems 152, *152*
    groundwater circulation well 150
    health and safety 158
    hot water flushing *152*, 153-5
    information requirements 158-60
    laboratory support 157
    limitations 160-1
    microbial treatment 146-8, *156*
    National Rivers Authority,
        consultation with 143
    oxidation/oxygen enhancement 145,
        145B, *156*
        with hydrogen peroxide 147
        with microbubbles 147B
    permeable active barriers 151-3, *154*,
        156, *159*
    planning and management 156-7
    polymerisation of spilt monomer, using
        146B, *156*
    precipitation using caustic solutions
        146
    principle 143-4
    prognosis 161
    quality management 158
    reduction and double decomposition
        146
    site characterisation 158
    site requirements 157
    steam water flushing *152*, 153-5
    surfactant mobilisation 155
    treatment applicability matrix 8
    treatment methods 3
    vacuum vaporiser well 150, *150*, *151*
groundwater table, and SVE 80
Groveland Well Site, Massachusetts
    vapour extraction project 95B

halogenated/non-halgenated
    volatiles/semi-volatiles, elements and
    compounds of 164-5Ap
health and safety
    biological treatment/remediation 64
    chemical treatment 45
    electro-remediation, in-situ 137
    groundwater remediation, in-situ 158
    leaching/washing/flushing 23
    occupational 6
    soil vapour extraction (SVE) 85
    stabilisation/solidification, in-situ 127
    thermal desorption 105
    vitrification, in-situ (ISV) 116
Health and Safety at Work Act (1974),
    Duty of Care 6
Henry's Law Constant 86, 86B, 87B,
    169Ap
Hill Air Force Base, Utah, bioventing at
    56B
horizontal well drilling *10*
hot water flushing, groundwater
    remediation, in-situ *152*, 153-5
hydrofracturing *10*, 11B
hydrogen peroxide, oxidation with 35,
    147
hydrolysis 34B, 35B
Hyperventilate decision support software
    82B, 89-90
hypochlorite, with oxidation 35

information requirements
    biological treatment/remediation 64-5,
        65B
    chemical treatment 45, *45*
    electro-remediation 138
    groundwater remediation 158-60
    leaching/washing/flushing 23-5, *24*
    oxidation 45B
    polymerisation *45*
    reduction 45B
    soil vapour extraction (SVE) 86-9
    stabilisation/solidification 129B
    thermal desorption 105
    vitrification, in-situ (ISV) 116
information sources *5*
International Waste Technologies and
    Geo Con Inc stabilisation method 121,
    122, 122B
ion exchange resins, applicability *9*, *41*

kerfing *10*

laboratory support
    biological treatment/remediation 64

chemical treatment 44
electro-remediation 137
groundwater remediation 157
leaching/washing/flushing 23
soil vapour extraction (SVE) 85
stabilisation/solidification 128
thermal desorption 105
vitrification, in-situ (ISV) 116
leaching/washing/flushing, in-situ
applicability *9*
with carbon dioxide flushing 20B
costs 29
effectiveness 25
environmental protection 22-3
health and safety 23
with hydraulic containment *19*
information requirements 23-5, *24*
laboratory support 23
limitations 26
method description 18-20
monitoring 23
planning and management 20-1
plant and equipment 22
procurement 21
prognosis 29
quality management 23
site characterisation 23-4
site requirements 22
with spray irrigation containment *19*
surfactant selection criteria for oil *25*
technical specifications 21B
with temporary wall containment *19*
treatability studies 25
with trench containment *19*
legal requirements 4-5
light non-aqueous phase liquids
(LNAPLs) 150-1, 152
lime/liming
applicability *9*
used to raise pH to treat heavy metals
32, *41*

metals, heavy
treated with cation exchange 32
treated with lime 32
treated with organic matter 32
metals, volatile/non-volatile, elements
and compounds of 166Ap
methods integration 15
microbial treatment
at depth application 51-3
bioventing 53, *54*, 55B
co-metabolism *51*, *62*
colloidal gas aphrons *51*, *62*
genetically engineered microbes *51*

groundwater 146-8
groundwater remediation 146-8, *156*
limitations 68, *69*
oxygen level control *51*
oxygen sources *52*
soil property modification *51*
surface application 50-1
monitoring 14-15
electro-remediation 137
leaching/washing/flushing 23
soil vapour extraction (SVE) 90-1, 90B

National Rivers Authority 143

occupational health and safety 6
oil removal, surfactant selection for *25*
oil, waste, refinery site, bioremediation
for 55B
operational considerations 12-13
owners/occupiers duties, and public
health 6
oxidation
applicability *9*
groundwater remediation 147, *156*
with hydrogen peroxide 35, 35B, 36B
with hypochlorite 35
information requirements 45B
limitations *46*
with microbubbles 147B
with ozone 35
principle 33, 34B
rate of 33
restrictions 33
soil catalysed 34, 34B, *41*
oxidisers, elements and compounds of
166Ap
oxygen level control, microbial treatment
51
oxygen sources, microbial treatment *52*
ozone, oxidation with 35

Parsons Chemical Inc, Michigan,
vitrification at 117
PCBs
dechlorination by APEG process 39B,
41
dehalogenation chemically 32
elements and compounds of 165Ap
laboratory studies of flushing 29B
reduction with sodium borohydride
39B
and stabilisation 123, *124*
white rot fungi degradation 61B
performance testing 14-15
permeable active barriers, groundwater

remediation, in-situ 151-3, *154, 156*
pesticides
  elements and compounds of 165Ap
  hydrolysis of with sodium hydroxide 35B
  vitrification efficiency *117*
petrol contamination in Netherlands, bioremediation for 55B
petroleum hydrocarbons, characteristics 170Ap
photolysis, applicability *9*
planning and development control 6
planning and management
  biological treatment/remediation 61-2
  chemical treatment 40-3
  electro-remediation 136
  groundwater remediation 156-7
  leaching/washing/flushing 20-1
  soil vapour extraction (SVE) 82-3
  vitrification, in-situ (ISV) 115
plant and equipment
  biological treatment 63
  chemical treatment 43
  electro-remediation, in-situ 137
  leaching/washing/flushing 22
  soil vapour extraction (SVE) 83-4, *84*
  stabilisation/solidification 125, *126, 127*
  thermal desorption *104*
  vitrification, in-situ (ISV) 115-16
plant uptake, biological treatment 59, *62*
pneumatic fracturing *10, 93*, 93B, 94B
polymerisation
  for acrylate monomer leak 40B
  applicability *9*
  ground water treatment, in-situ *156*
  information requirements *45*
  limitations *46*
  principle 39-40
pressure injection *10*
public health, and owners/occupiers duties 6

quality management
  biological treatment/remediation 64
  chemical treatment 44-5
  groundwater remediation, in-situ 158
  leaching/washing/flushing 23
  soil vapour extraction (SVE) 85
  stabilisation/solidification, in-situ 128
  vitrification, in-situ (ISV) 116

radial well drilling *10*
radio frequency heating, applicability *9*
radioactive materials, elements and

compounds of 166Ap
Raoult's law 168Ap
recovery systems for liquids 12-13, *13*
reducers, elements and compounds of 166Ap
reduction
  applicability *9*
  chromium, hexavalent 37-8, 38B
  environmental impacts 44B
  information requirements 45B
  iron powders, use of 36, 37B
  limitations *46*
  for organic compounds 36-7, 37B
  principle 36
  selenium, hexavalent 38-9
Resource Guides (USEPA) 5
root uptake, biological treatment 59

selenium, hexavalent, reduction of 38-9
shallow soil mixing (SSM) techniques 124
site characterisation
  groundwater remediation, in-situ 158
  leaching/washing/flushing 23-4
  physical 7
  soil vapour extraction (SVE) 86-9
site requirements
  biological treatment 63
  chemical treatment 43
  electro-remediation, in-situ 137
  groundwater remediation, in-situ 157
  leaching/washing/flushing 22
  soil vapour extraction (SVE) 83
  stabilisation/solidification, in-situ 125
  thermal desorption 104
  vitrification, in-situ (ISV) 115
sodium borohydride, dechlorination of PCBs 39B
soil, and in-situ treatment methods 3
soil cooling/freezing, applicability *9*
soil leaching/washing/flushing *see* leaching/washing/flushing
soil property modification, microbial treatment *51*
soil sorption coefficient 169Ap
soil vapour extraction (SVE), in-situ 53, *54*
  Aberdeen petroleum site case 78B
  advection-limited sites 91B
  with air sparging *76*
  applicability 78-82, *79*
  applications *9*, 15
  with bioventing 76B
  carbon adsorption 75
  contaminated groundwater from 75,

77B
costs 96
design guidance available 89-90
diffusion-limited sites 91B
effectiveness 80, 91-2, 93B, 94B, 95B
environmental protection 84
extraction well radius of influence 80B
with groundwater extraction 76B
health and safety 85
Hyperventilate decision support
  software 82B
information requirements 86-9
laboratory column tests 87
laboratory support 85
limitations 95-6
low air permeability sites 95
monitoring 90-1, 90B
Netherlands service station case 81,
  81B
pilot testing 87-9
planning and management 82-3
plant and equipment 83-4, 84
principle 73-7
process schematic 74
prognosis 96-7
quality management 85
site characterisation 86-9, 88
site requirements 83
system without air infiltration 74
technical specification 83
waste streams generated by 75
soil venting see soil vapour extraction
  (SVE)
Soilcrete jet grouting 122B
solidification see stabilisation/
  solidification, in-situ
stabilisation/solidification, in-situ
  applicability 9, 123-5
  costs 130-1
  deep soil mixing (DSM) 122, 124, 125,
    126
  effectiveness 129
  environmental protection 127
  health and safety 127
  information requirements 129B
  International Waste Technologies and
    Geo Con Inc method 121, 122, 122B,
    125
  laboratory support 128
  limitations 124-5, 130
  plant and equipment 125, 126, 127
  principle 121
  process 121, 122
  product obtained 123
  prognosis 131

· quality management 128
  shallow mixing systems (SMS) 124,
    125
  site requirements 125
  slurry mixing unit 126
steam stripping, stationary 102-3, 103,
  104
steam water flushing, groundwater
  remediation, in-situ 152, 153-5
steam/hot air stripping, mobile 100-2,
  101, 103, 104
streaming potential 133
subsurface heating 77
surface soils, chemical treatment 44B
surfactant mobilisation, groundwater
  remediation, in-situ 155

technical specifications
  biological treatment 62-3
  soil vapour extraction (SVE) 83
Technology Evaluation Reports (USEPA)
  5
thermal desorption, in-situ
  applicability 9, 103-4, 103
  costs 107
  effectiveness 105-6, 106
  environmental protection 105
  health and safety 105
  information requirements 105
  laboratory support 105
  limitations 106
  mobile steam/hot air stripping 100-2,
    101, 103, 104
  plant and equipment 104
  principle 100
  prognosis 1-7
  site requirements 104
  stationary steam stripping 102-3, 103,
    104
Thomas Solvent Raymond Road (TSRR)
  vapour extraction project 94B
toxaphene contamination 37B
treatability studies
  biological treatment 65-6
  leaching/washing/flushing 25

ultrasonic methods 10
United Chrome Superfund site,
  chromium contamination treatment 28B
Unterdruck-Verdampf-Brunnen (UVB)
  system 150, 151
US Environmental Protection Agency
  (USEPA) 5, 89, 92, 97
US National Research Council (NRC) 66

vacuum vaporiser well, groundwater
   remediation 150, *150, 151*
vadose zone, contaminant behaviour
   air permeability 167Ap
   contaminant composition 171Ap
   Henry's law 169Ap
   soil heterogeneity 167-8Ap
   soil sorption coefficient 169Ap
   vapour pressure in 168Ap
   vapour transport 172Ap
   water content 168Ap
   water solubility 169Ap
vapour extraction *see* soil vapour
   extraction (SVE)
vapour pressure, and Raoult's Law
   168Ap
vapour transport, and Darcy's Law
   172Ap
vegetation uptake, biological treatment
   57-60
Vendor Information System for
   Innovative Treatment Technologies
   (VISITT) 5
vitrification, in-situ (ISV)
   applicability *9*, 113-15
   contaminant removal/destruction
     processes 111

costs 119
effectiveness 117, *117, 118*
environmental protection 116
health and safety 116
information requirements 116
laboratory support 116
limitations 118
off-gas treatment *113*
planning and management 115
plant and equipment 115-16
power for 116
principle 109
process 109-13, *112*
prognosis 120
quality management 116
residual product 113
site requirements 115
volatile organic compounds (VOCs) 74
volatiles/non volatiles, vitrification
   efficiency *117*

washing *see* leaching/washing/flushing
Water Industry Act (1991) 7
Water Resources Act (1991) 7
water solubility 169Ap
white rot fungi, biological treatment 60,
   61B

10 Volume X Special situations SP110

Volume X provides information and guidance on the management of situations that are outside the classic redevelopment scenario. It addresses:

- temporary and emergency actions

- operating or already developed sites in which remedial action may be constrained by the presence of buildings, process plant, and occupational or residential use etc.

- infrastructure projects taking place over, under, or in contaminated ground

- construction operations on reclaimed sites where contaminants remain in place under the protection of a containment, or similar, system

- 'problem' sites – i.e. those contaminated sites where there is no formal development use in place, but which nevertheless are deemed to be posing unacceptable public health risks or environmental impacts.

The typical problems that such sites present for site investigations, risk assessment and selection, design and implementation activities are reviewed (using case studies where available) and guidance on appropriate procedures are given.

CONTENTS

1 **INTRODUCTION**
   1.1   Scope
   1.2   Special situations
   1.3   Building on contaminated sites
   References

2 **INFRASTRUCTURE PROJECTS**
   2.1   Introduction
   2.2   Route selection
   2.3   Site investigation
   2.4   Hazard and risk assessment
   2.5   Design of principal works
   References

3 **OPERATING SITES**
   3.1   Introduction
   3.2   Site investigation
   3.3   Remedial works
   3.4   Design of principal works

4 **SITES ALREADY DEVELOPED FOR SENSITIVE USES**
   4.1   Introduction
   4.2   Occurrence of contamination in urban areas

4.3   Social impacts

4.4   Community relations

4.5   Site investigation and assessment

4.6   Remedial works

References

5 'PROBLEM' SITES

5.1   Introduction

5.2   Site investigation

5.3   Temporary and short term remedial measures

5.4   Long-term and permanent remedial measures

References

6 BUILDING ON CONTAMINATED SITES

6.1   Introduction

6.2   Interaction with construction works

6.3   The already reclaimed site

6.4   Selection and protection of building materials

6.5   Implementation

Reference

REFERENCES

ANON. *A survey of Gassing Landfills sites in England and Wales.* Friends of the Earth (London), 1992

ANON. *Digest 363: Sulphate and acid resistance of concrete in the ground.* Building Research Establishment (Garston), 1991

ANON. Tarmac takes Express tunnel. *New Civil Engineer*, 1993 (18 Nov), 6

ANON. The Jubilee Line Extension. *New Civil Engineer* Supplement, February, 1994

ANON. *Water lines in contaminated soil.* Report No. 87. Keuringsinstituut voor waterleidingartikelen KIWA nv (Nieuwegein, The Netherlands), 1985

BARRY, D.L. *Material durability in aggressive ground.* Report 98. CIRIA (London), 1983

BUILDING RESEARCH ESTABLISHMENT. *Construction of New Buildings on Gas-contaminated Land.* Building Research Establishment (Garston), 1991

CAIRNEY, T. (ed.) *Contaminated Land: Problems and Solutions.* Blackie Academic and Professional (Glasgow), 1993

CARD, G.B. *Protecting development from methane.* Report 149. CIRIA (London), 1995

CARTER, M. Restoration of a toxic waste quarry. *J.Environ. Management.* 1979, **9** (2), 123-128

COONEY, P. Contaminated sites – local authority experience. In: *Proceedings of a Conference on Redevelopment of Contaminated Land.* London Borough of Greenwich (Woolwich), 1982

COPPIN, N.J., STAFF, M.G. and BROWN, C.W. Snailbeach – the environmental impact of an abandoned lead mine. In: *Proceedings of an International Conference on Construction on Polluted and Marginal Land*. Engineering Technics Press (Edinburgh), 1990, pp 159-170

CRATHORNE, B., De ROSA, J., FIELDING, M. and HETHERINGTON, J. *The effects of contaminants on materials used for distribution of water*. Water Research Centre (Swindon), 1987

DAVIES, B.E. Plant-available lead and other metals in British garden soils. *Science of the Total Environment*, 1978, **9**, 243-262

DENNER, J.M., STERRITT, R.M. and PERRY, R. *Study on hazardous wastes and the public – social, psychological, economic and health aspects of contaminated land and waste disposal facilities in the UK*. European Foundation for Improvement in Living and Working Conditions (Dublin)

DEPARTMENT OF THE ENVIRONMENT/WELSH OFFICE. *Approved Document C: Site Preparation and Resistance to Moisture*. HMSO (London), 1992

DEPARTMENT OF THE ENVIRONMENT/WELSH OFFICE. *Landfill Sites: Development Control*. DOE Circular 17/89, WO Circular 38/89. HMSO (London), 1989

DEPARTMENT OF TRANSPORT, DEPARTMENT OF THE ENVIRONMENT, PROPERTY SERVICES AGENCY, SCOTTISH DEVELOPMENT DEPARTMENT, WELSH OFFICE, DEPARTMENT OF THE ENVIRONMENT FOR NORTHERN IRELAND. *Specification and method of measurement for ground investigation*. HMSO (London), 1987

DEPARTMENT OF TRANSPORT. *Manual of Contract Documents for Highway Works. Volume Specification for Highway Works (December 1991)*. MCHW1. HMSO (London), reprint 1993

ELLIS, A.C. and DYSON, A.D. Black Country Spine Road Investigation: Chemical Aspects. In: *Proceedings of a Conference on Contaminated Land, Policy, Regulation and Technology, London 1991*. IBC Technical Services (London), 1991

FLEMING, G. (ed.). *Recycling Derelict Land*. Thomas Telford (London), 1991

GABRYLISZYN, J. The design of a road cutting through a contaminated waste tip. In: *Building on Marginal and Derelict Land*. Thomas Telford (London), 1986, pp 297-314

GARVIN, S., HARTLESS, R.P. and PAUL, V. The Building Research Establishment's Research Programme on Contaminated Land, 1991. In: *Proceedings of a Conference on Contaminated Land: Policy, Regulation and Technology*. IBC Technical Services (London), 1991

General Development Order 1988. HMSO (London), 1988

HEALTH AND SAFETY COMMISSION. *Construction (Design and Management) Regulations 1994*. HMSO (London), 1994

HEALTH AND SAFETY EXECUTIVE. *Control of Substances Hazardous to Health Regulations, 1994*. HMSO (London)

HEALTH AND SAFETY EXECUTIVE. *Protection of personnel and the general public during development of contaminated land.* HS(6)66. HMSO (London), 1991

HEALTH AND SAFETY EXECUTIVE. *Protection of workers and the general public during the development of contaminated land.* H(G)66. HMSO (London), 1991

HEASMAN, L. Structured risk assessment procedure to categorise sites which may be contaminated. In: *Proceedings of a Seminar on Contaminated Land: The Planning Dilemma.* Laboratory of the Government Chemist (London)/Aspinwall & Co (Shrewsbury), 1993

HIGHWAYS AGENCY. *Draft Advice Note: Site Investigation for Highway Works.* Highways Agency (London), 1994

HOOMANS, J.P. and STELLINGWERFF (ed.). Operation Lekkerkerk West. *Pt/civiele Techniek,* 1982, (1), 3-44 (available in Building Research Establishment translation)

KHAN, A.Q. Investigation and treatment of Ravenfield tip. In: *Reclamation of Contaminated Land.* Society of Chemical Industry (London), 1980, pp F3/1-11

LEACH, B.A. and GOODGER, H.K. *Building on Derelict Land.* Special Publication 78. CIRIA (London), 1991

LONGLANDS, H.G. and TOWNSEND, G.H. Sewerage with particular reference to the Beckton development in East London. In: *Reclamation of Contaminated Land.* Society of Chemical Industry (London), 1980, pp E2/1-11

PAUL, V. *A Review of the Performance of Materials of Construction in Aggressive Soils.* Building Research Establishment (Garston), 1994

SMITH, L.C. Hazards to immediate workers on site. In: *Reclamation of Contaminated Land,* pp D1/1-11. Society of Chemical Industry (London), 1980.

SMITH, M.A. An international study on social aspects etc of contaminated land. In: *Contaminated Soil '88.* K. Wolf *et al* (ed.). Kluwer Academic Publishers (Dordrecht), 1988, pp 415-424

SMITH, M.A. and BAKER, S.B. An international study of the social aspects etc. of problem hazardous waste sites. In: *Proceedings of Superfund '87.* Hazardous Materials Control Research Institute (Silver Spring, Maryland), 1987, pp 264-267

SMITH, M.A. and BAKER, S.B. The social impacts etc. of polluted sites: public involvement. In: *Proceedings of LAND REC '88.* Durham County Council (Durham), 1988, pp 25-34

SMITH, M.A. and BAKER, S.B. *Social, psychological and economic aspects of contaminated land.* (Report for the European Foundation for Improvement of Living and Working Conditions). Clayton Bostock Hill & Rigby (Birmingham), 1987

SMITH, M.A., BAKER, S.B. and POPE, W. The public perception of risks associated with the re-use of waste disposal sites. In: *Proceedings of Safewaste 87.* Industrial Seminars Ltd (Tunbridge Wells), 1987, pp 219-224

SMITH, M.A. Data analysis and interpretation. In: *Recycling Derelict and Marginal Land*. G. Fleming (ed.). Thomas Telford (London), 1991, pp 88-144

STEEDS, J.E., SHEPHERD, E. and BARRY, D.L. *A guide to safe working practices for contaminated sites*. Report 132. CIRIA (London), 1996

THE SCOTTISH OFFICE. *Technical Standards for Compliance with the Building Standards (Scotland) Regulations 1990*. Standard G2 and associated Appendix. HMSO (Edinburgh), 1990

WELSH OFFICE. *Halkyn Mountain Project Report*. Welsh Office (Cardiff), 1983

WILSON, D.C. and SMITH, E.T. Uncontrolled hazardous waste sites – a perspective of the problem in the UK. In: *Proceedings of a Conference on Management of Uncontrolled Hazardous Waste Sites, Washington DC 1980*. Hazardous Materials Control Research Institute (Silver Spring, Maryland), 1980, pp 8-14

INDEX

Note: Numbers in italics refer to Tables. B indicates a Box, and Ap indicates an Appendix

air sparging *16*
biological treatment *15*
   residential and other developed sites *26*
Black Country Spine Road 4, *5*
building materials, selection and protection of 42-5
   design solutions 44-5
   performance under aggressive ground conditions *43*
Building Regulations 43
   requirements for residual contamination 38

chemical treatment *15*
   residential and other developed sites *26*
civil engineering methods, operating sites *13*
communications, importance of 46
communities
   and individuals, economic costs of contaminated sites 19-20
   typical effects of contaminated sites 19
community relations, importance of regarding contaminated sites 20
compatibility issues, already reclaimed sites 41-2
construction, effective, principal considerations 45
Construction (Design and Management) Regulations 43

construction materials, appropriate 36
construction works
   designed to avoid spread of contamination 16
   interaction with contamination 36, 37-9
   new, aspects to be addressed 16
contaminants, general urban 18
contaminated material
   leaving in place vs. excavation 8
   low-level contamination, use of in landscaping bunds and sound barriers 9
   potential difficulty of excavation, disposal or re-use 9
contaminated sites
   building on 2-3, 36-46
     the already reclaimed site 39-42
     implementation 45-6
     interaction with construction work 37-9
     selection and protection of building materials 42-5
   designing services for 38
   threats from 19
contamination
   implications of leaving in place 3
   interaction with construction work 36, 37-9
   left in place 14
     will construction work compromise the remedial work 41-2

local 21
long-term impacts and liabilities 8
occurrence of in urban areas 18
cost/risk judgements 43
Coventry Bypass, waste disposal site
found during site investigation *5*
cover, temporary 38
covering systems *13*
and later foundations 42

demolition, may be cheaper than
remediation 23
Department of Transport, Specification
for Highway Works 9
derelict land, factors considered for
infrastructure project selection 4, 6B
desk studies 6, 18
route selection, infrastructure projects
4, *6*
development, some time after
remediation 36
dust blow, prevention of 31
dust contamination, urban 21
dynamic compaction, effects on
contamination 37-8

electro-remediation *15*
emergency action programme, to secure
site 29
engineering methods *32*
Environmental Protection Act (EPA)
(1990) 17
Section 143 18
ex-situ treatment
of groundwaters *32*
methods for operating sites *13*
residential and other developed sites
26
of soils *32*
excavated material, assessment of
acceptability for re-use 9
excavation *13*

Fetters Hill Quarry, Forest of Dean,
problem site 34B
foams, for temporary covering 31B
foundations 41, 42
interaction with remaining
contaminants 37-8

gas monitoring boreholes 29-30
ground compaction, carried out before
covering 38
ground improvement, interaction with
remaining contaminants 37-8

groundwater
determination of quality 7
ex-situ treatment *14, 32*
groundwater monitoring wells 29, 30

hazard assessment, initial 22
hazard ranking, preliminary 30
hazard ranking systems 18
hazard and risk
of building materials in contaminated
ground 43
problem sites
arising from buried material 29
determination of 29, 30
hazard and risk assessment,
infrastructure projects 7
hazardous waste disposal site, disused 28
concept for long-term problem
amelioration 33B
Heathrow Express link, contamination a
major issue *5*
housing
remediation options 22-3, *25-6*
subsequently found to be on
contaminated land 24B
hydraulic controls *13*
hydraulic regime, characterisation of 7

in-situ treatment
of groundwater *16, 32*
residential and other developed sites
26
of soils etc. *15, 32*
industrial site, abandoned 28
infiltration rates 37
infrastructure projects 1, 4-10
design of principal works 8-10, 14, 16
hazard and risk assessment 7
route selection 4, 6
site investigation 6-7
inundation, and groundwater
contamination 37

Jubilee Line extension, contamination a
major issue *5*

liabilities
arising from purchase/leasing of
already reclaimed sites 40
longer-term, expense of failure to
recognise 8-9
litigation, special care needed in
unravelling contamination sources 21

Malkins Bank, Cheshire, problem site

34B

materials
   choice/quality with/without protection, determination of 44
   durability below ground 44
   performance in practice 45
migration, of chemical contaminants and gases, protection from 8
monitoring
   investigation of problem sites 29-30
   long-term capability 14
monitoring points, permanent 14
motorways, infrastructure projects where contamination a major issue *5*

off-site processing *13*
on-site processing *13*
operational/operating sites 2, 11-16
   remedial works 12-14, *15-16*
      potentially applicable methods *13-14, 15-16*
   site investigation 11-12

piles/piling 42
   and contaminant migration 37
planning permission, does not guarantee remediated site suitable for specified purpose 41
preliminary surveys 6
prevention of, dust blow 31
problem sites 2, 28-33
   general investigation procedure 29
   investigation and assessment requires specialists skills and careful handling 17
   long-term/permanent remedial measures 31-3
   may require immediate and long-term measures 28
   with mixed wastes, remedy selection for *32*
   objectives of investigations 28
   out-of-site investigations 29
   site investigation 29-30
   some UK sites *34*
   temporary/short-term remedial measures 30-1
   in the UK 34B
protective systems 45
public road construction, site investigation specifications 7

quality assurance 44, 46

Ravenfield Tip, S. Yorks, problem site

·34B

reclaimed sites 39-42
   compatibility of construction works 41-2
   establishing nature of works already done 40-1
   initial appraisal 39-40
   likely investigations 41
   site management 42
   some development examples *40*
remedial measures
   long-term and permanent 31-3
   temporary and short-term 30-1
remedial works, operating sites 12-14, *15-16*
remediation
   and construction, as part of an overall development 3
   and development, as part of an integrated programme 36
   for future development 3
risk assessment, preliminary 30
risk estimates
   consequences of materials failure 44
   contamination affecting gardens 20-1
risk perception, of families and communities 19
roads, placement over contaminated areas 9
route selection, infrastructure projects 4, 6

safety, an important issue 36
sealing, to reduce filtration 14
sealing/covering surfaces 30
sensitive uses, sites already developed for 2, 17-26
   health/social aspects of site investigations 17
   occurrence of contamination in urban areas 18
   remedial works 22-3, *25-6*
   site investigation and assessment 20-2
   social impacts of polluted sites 19-20
   triggers for investigation 17
service provision 42
   early detailed design 39
   using common conduits 39
services
   in back-filled trenches 39
   design considerations 38-9
   ideally not placed in contaminated ground 39
   in-ground replaced by above ground 14
site control, stepwise approach 30-1

site investigation
    and assessment, sites already
        developed for sensitive uses 20-2
    infrastructure projects 6-7
    operating sites 11-12
    problem sites 29-30
        on-site investigation should
            minimise disturbance 30
site reconnaissance 6
soil flushing/washing *15*
soil vapour extraction *15*
special situations 1-3
    building on contaminated sites 2-3, 36-
        46
    infrastructure projects 1, 4-10
    operational/operating sites 2, 11-16
    problem sites 2, 28-33, *34*
    sites already developed for sensitive
        uses 2, 17-26
stone columns, and contaminant
    migration 37
supervision, care required 46
surface water run-off 42

thermal desorption *15*
Transport, Department of, Specification
    for Highway Works 9
transport routes, key issues in route
    selection and for design purposes 6B, 8
tunnel construction, possible higher level
    contamination 7
tunnelling projects 9-10
    route selection/design factors to be
        addressed 9

urban areas
    occurrence of contamination in 18
    required site investigations 20
    surveys to identify potentially
        contaminated sites 18
urban contamination, general 18

vertical barriers *13*, 42
    relationship with ground improvement
        38
vitrification *15*

waste regulation authorities, survey and
    screening process, potentially gassing
    landfill sites 18
water supply pipes, and contaminated
    ground 39

11 Volume XI Planning and management SP111

Volume XI stresses the importance of good planning and management and highlights the issues that should be addressed throughout the remediation process. Subjects covered include the definition of project goals and objectives, project planning, procurement, contractual aspects and implementation. The role of quality management systems, and their application to contaminated land projects, is reviewed.

CONTENTS

1 **PROJECT FRAMEWORK**
    1.1   What is a project?
    1.2   Project goals
    1.3   Planning a project
    1.4   Procurement
    1.5   Implementation
    1.6   Quality management systems
    References

2 **OBJECTIVES AND SPECIFICATION**
    2.1   Overall goals
    2.2   Technical objectives
    2.3   Management objectives
    2.4   Specification
    References

3 **PLANNING**
    3.1   Overall project planning
    3.2   Building the team
    3.3   Planning resources
    3.4   Preparation of detailed plans
    References

4 **PROCUREMENT**
    4.1   Project organisation
    4.2   Contractual arrangements
    4.3   Selection of advisers and contractors
    References

5 **IMPLEMENTATION**
    5.1   Overall scope
    5.2   Supervision
    5.3   Communication
    5.4   Monitoring and review
    5.5   Documentation
    References

6 QUALITY MANAGEMENT SYSTEMS
6.1   Description
6.2   Interaction with contracts
References

Appendix 1   Contractual arrangements
Appendix 2   Alternative contractual approaches
Appendix 3   Quality management systems

REFERENCES

A Client's Guide to Quality Assurance in Construction. Special Publication 55. CIRIA (London), 1988

ASHFORD, J.L. *Quality management in construction – certification of product quality and quality management systems.* Special Publication 72. CIRIA (London), 1989

BARBER, J.N. *Quality management in construction – contractual aspects.* Special Publication 84. CIRIA (London), 1992

BRITISH STANDARDS INSTITUTION
BS 5750 *Quality systems*
Part 0 *Principal concepts and applications*
Part 0.1 *Guide to selection and use* (ISO 9000)
Part 0.2 *Guide to quality management and quality system elements* (ISO 9004)
Part 1 *Specification for design/development, production, installation and servicing* (ISO 9001)
Part 2 *Specification for production and installation* (ISO 9002)
Part 3 *Specification for final installation and test* (ISO 9003)
Part 4 *Guide to the use of BS 5750, Parts 1, 2, and 3*
BSI (London) 1987 (Part 4, 1990)

BRITISH STANDARDS INSTITUTION. *Preparation of Specifications.* BS 7373. BSI (London), 1991

BRITISH STANDARDS INSTITUTION. *Specification for Environment Management Systems.* BS 7750 BSI (London), 1992

CAIRNEY, T. (ed.) *Contaminated Land: Problems and Solutions.* Blackie Academic and Professional (Glasgow), 1993

CHARTERED INSTITUTE OF BUILDING. *Code of Practice for Project Management for Construction and Development.* CIOB, 1992

CLARK, R.C., PLEDGER, M. and NEEDLER, H.M.J. Risk analysis in the evaluation of non-aerospace projects. *International Journal of Project Management*, **8**, No. 1, February 1990

DEPARTMENT OF TRANSPORT. *Specification for Ground Investigation.* HMSO (London), 1987

DEPARTMENT OF TRANSPORT. *Specification for Highway Works.* Seventh edition. HMSO (London), 1991

DINSMORE, P.C. Ideas, guidelines and techniques for applying project management solutions in the general business arena: lessons for executives. *International Journal of Project Management*, **8**, No. 1, February 1990

FLEMING, G. (ed.). *Recycling Derelict Land.* Thomas Telford (London), 1991

HASWELL, C.K. and DE SILVA, D.S. *Civil Engineering Contracts: Practice and Procedure.* Second Edition. Butterworths, 1989

INSTITUTION OF CIVIL ENGINEERS. *Specification for Ground Improvement.* Thomas Telford (London), 1989

INSTITUTION OF CIVIL ENGINEERS. *Specification for Piling.* Thomas Telford (London), 1988

LEACH, B.A. and GOODGER, H.K. *Building on Derelict Land.* Special Publication 78. CIRIA (London), 1991

MARSH, P.D.V. *Contracting for Engineering and Construction Projects.* Third edition. Gower, 1988

MORGAN, M.G. Risk analysis and management. *Scientific American,* July 1993

OLIVER, G.B.M. *Quality management in construction: Interpretation of BS 5750 (1987) – quality management for the construction industry.* Special Publication 74. CIRIA (London), 1990

RANDOLPH, W.A. and POSNER, B.Z. *Effective Project Planning and Management.* Prentice Hall International Editions, 1988

SITE INVESTIGATION STEERING GROUP. *Specification. Site Investigation in Construction,* Volume 3. Thomas Telford (London), 1993

SPENCE WATSON, J. Steps towards a coherent Scottish approach. In: *IBC Conference Proceedings 5th Annual Conference. Contaminated Land: Policy, Risk Management and Technology.* IBC Technical Services (London), 1994

UFF, J.F. and CLAYTON, C.R.I. *Role and responsibility in site investigation.* Special Publication 73. CIRIA (London), 1991

WEARNE, S. *Civil engineering contracts.* Thomas Telford (London), 1989

INDEX

Note: Numbers in italics refer to Tables. B indicates a Box, and Ap indicates an Appendix

admeasurement contracts 28, 48Ap, 52Ap, 53Ap
advisers *23*
  contracts for 27B
  providing professional services 24
  selection of 31-2
appendices 40B

Association of Consulting Engineers Agreement 1 49Ap
Association of Consulting Engineers guidelines 32
Association of Environmental Consultancies (AEC) advisers, selection of 31-2

Bill of Quantities 48Ap, 52Ap
  and methods of measurement 53-4Ap
breach of contract 25
BS 5750 6, 58Ap
  obligation to identify and record all
    reference documents 40-1
BS 7750 6

Chartered Institute of Building Code of
  Practice on Project Management 16
Civil Engineering Standard Form of
  Measurement 28
Civil Engineers Standard Method of
  Measurement (CESMM) 53Ap
clients 23-4, *23*
  objectives 23
  selection of advisers and contractors
    31-2
  to specify documentation requirements
    41
commercial risk, for ground remedial
  work 5, 25-6
communication 6, 36-7
  with external parties 37
  internal communications requirements
    37
  need for clear instructions 36
  poor, leading to design and
    construction faults 43, *44*
  to overcome negative attention 36-7
completion reports 41
  examples of reports included 40B
compliance monitoring 57Ap
construction management contracts
  49Ap, *50Ap*
contaminated land projects
  advantages and disadvantages of
    different organisational approaches
    29B
  bodies involved in design and
    execution of 22-4, *23*
  criteria for selection of
    individuals/organisations 5
  defects in from design and
    construction faults 43, *44*, 45B
  design and implement approach 28
  examples *2*
    of end results 3, 4B
    where specifications could be
      produced 10B
  guidance for suitable organisations 32
  importance of rules on limitation 30
  interested bodies 22
  management objectives 9

need for accurate records 38
quality management systems require
  adjustment 42
remedial works contract as a separate
  package 25
scope for errors 36
traditional approach 28, 29B
types of information to be recorded 39
typical characteristics 1
contaminated material, excavation of for
  on- or off-site disposal 13B
contingency planning 4, 19, 20-1
  examples of possible requirement *20*
contract documents, principal
  components 51Ap
contract law, a civil matter 28-9
contractors *23*
  contracts for 27B
  role of 24
  selection of 31-2
contracts 5
  allowing for the unexpected 25
  alternative approach 55-7Ap
  components of, documents 51-2Ap
  and contractors 31
  documents include a specification 10
  enforceability limited by statute 30
  forms/types of 27-8, 48-51Ap
  General Conditions of Contract 52Ap
  limitations of 28-30
  purpose of 26-7
  quality framework provided by 43B
  review of, required by a Quality
    Management System 59B
  separate for each phase 5
  Special Conditions of Contract 52Ap
  standard conditions of contract *53*Ap
  traditional approach 55Ap, 57Ap
  use of 25-6
cost planning, detailed 19
cost/reimbursement contracts 48Ap
covering systems, placement of, standard
  specifications 13B
critical path analysis *3*, 4
current status reports 40B

decommissioning, decontamination and
  demolition reports 40B
Design Brief 10
design and build approach 14
design and build contracts 55Ap
design and construction faults, resulting
  from poor communication 43, *44*
design control, in a Quality Management
  System 59B

design and implement approach 14, 28, 29B
design and implement contracts 36, 48Ap, 53Ap, 54Ap
  advantages and disadvantages 56Ap
  clarity in specification and contract documentation essential 57Ap
design and investigate contracts 55Ap
design and procurement, detailed reports 40B
design and remediate approach 55Ap
design warranties 26-7
detailed plans, preparation of 19-21
  contingency planning 20-1
  licences and permissions 19-20
document control, in a Quality Management System 60B
documentation 6
  completion reports 41
  as components of a contracts 51-2Ap
  information requirements 39-41
  project records 38-9
  in quality management systems 44

earthworks scheme, method-based or performance-based specification 12-13
'Engineer' 31
  duties of 35-6
Europe, joint contractual approach 28
evaluation system for submissions from consultants (Scottish Enterprise) 32, 33

flow charts 3, 4
Form of Bond 52Ap
Form of Tender 52Ap

Gantt (bar) charts 4
ground remedial works, options for managing commercial risk 25-6
guarantees/indemnities 26, 27

ICE Conditions of Contract 28
implementation 35-41
  aspects of 6
  communication 36-7
  documentation 38-41
  monitoring and review 37-8
  supervision 35-6
indemnities 27
information requirements 39-41
inspection and testing, in a Quality Management System 61B
Institution of Chemical Engineers Model Contract 53Ap
Institution of Civil Engineers Conditions

of Contract 28, 52Ap
Instructions to Tenderers 51Ap
insurance
  availability of 30-1
  limit and extent of, used as criterion for selection of professional advisers 32
International Organisation for Standardisation (ISO), developing analytical methods for contaminated land application 11

land remediation, selection of Conditions of Contract 52Ap
land remediation projects, specified performance parameters 13-14
Latent Damage Act (1986) 30
licences/permissions 19-20
Limitation Act (1980) 30
local communities 22
lump sum contracts 28, 36, 48Ap, 50Ap, 51Ap, 53Ap, 53-4Ap

machinery 18
management contracts 49Ap
management objectives 8, 9
management planning 16-21
management responsibility, in a Quality Management System 59B
materials 18
measurement, standard methods of 54Ap
monitoring
  early arrangements for 38
  long-term
    contractual arrangements for 27
    length of time records to be held 41
  and review 6, 37-8

New Engineering Contract 53Ap
non-conforming products, control of, in a Quality Management System 62B

objectives
  in contaminated land projects 3, 4B
  setting of (SMART) 8
overall goals 8-9

percentage-based contracts 51Ap
performance over time, period of maintenance equalling period of guarantee/indemnity 27
personnel 18
piled walls, installation of, standard specifications 13B
pilot scheme operations 56Ap

planning 15-21
    overall project planning 15-17
    planning resources 17-19
    preparation of detailed plans 19-21
    in the project cycle 17
    team building 17
planning permission and/or contract
    documents 39
planning resources 17-19
process control, in a Quality Management
    System 60B
process-based techniques, Conditions of
    Contract 52-3Ap
procurement 5, 22-33, *34*
    contractual arrangements 25-31
    project organisation 22-5
    referring to appointment of
        professional advisers 32
    relating to appointment of a contractor
        31
    selection of advisers and contractors
        31-2
product identification and traceability, in
    a Quality Management System 60B
professional indemnity insurance 32
    re contamination incidents, withdrawal
        of 30-1
    uncertainty over future market
        availability 32
progress meetings, to support monitoring
    and review 38
progress reports 40B
project, defined 1
project flow chart 2, *3*
project framework 1-7
    implementation 6
    planning 3-5
    procurement 5
    project goals 2
    quality management systems 6-7
project goals 3
    characteristics to be effective
        (SMART) 8
project life cycle 1
    contracts 25-6
    planning in 17
project management
    effective 2
        requirements for 17
    key objectives 16
project manager 4-5
    duties 24-5
    a vital appointment 24
project organisation 22-5
    roles and responsibilities defined

contractually 22
project planning 3-5, 15-17
    advantages of 15
    alternative approaches 4
project records 38-9
project team, likely members 17
purchasing, in a Quality Management
    System 60B

QMS *see* quality management systems
quality assurance 58Ap
quality audits, in a Quality Management
    System 63B
quality control 58Ap
quality management 19
quality management provisions, problems
    with lack of care in translation into
    contractual obligations 45-6
quality management systems 6-7, 36, 42-
    6, 58Ap, 59-63B
    can redress design and construction
        fault problems 43-4
    interaction with contracts 43-6
    limitation of in contaminated land
        projects 7
    potential benefits to purchasing and
        supplying organisations 42
quality plan 19
quality records, in a Quality Management
    System 62B

regulatory requirements, may need
    specific procedures 37
remedial methods, selection of 40B
resource planning
    allowing for the unexpected 19
    machinery, materials, personnel *18*
resources, adequacy of 4
risk-sharing 5, 30-1

schedule of rates 48Ap
servicing, in a Quality Management
    System 63B
site investigation and assessment reports
    40B
site investigation reports 38
Site Investigation Steering Group (SISG),
    specification for site investigation
    (1993) 11
site investigations, use of SISG
    specification 13B
slurry walls, installation of, standard
    specifications 13B
special interest groups 22
special reports 41

specifications 9-14
    aspects to be considered *11*
    level of detail 13B
    method-based 12-13, 56Ap
    performance-based 13-14
    process-based 56Ap
standard contracts, and quality
    management standards 44, 46
standard specifications
    examples of use in contaminated land
        projects 13B
    UK 11, 12, *12*
statistical techniques, in a Quality
    Management System 63B
statutory bodies 22
subcontractors *23*, 24
supervision 6, 35-6
    good, implications of failure to supply
        35
    independent 36

· type and level of 35

team building 17
technical monitoring 38
technical objectives 8, 9, *11*
technical-managerial coordination
    lack of, possible problems 15B
    for successful planning 15
time basis contracts 49-50Ap
traditional approach 28, 29B, 55Ap,
    57Ap
training, in a Quality Management
    System 63B
treatability studies 56Ap
turnkey contracts 49Ap

validation, responsibility for 57Ap

warranties 26
    insurance-backed, availability of 30-1

12   Volume XII Policy and legislation SP112

This volume describes the policy, administration and legal framework for the management of contaminated land in the UK in terms of:

- planning and development control
- public health
- occupational health and safety
- environmental protection
- liability issues.

Specific arrangements for Scotland and Northern Ireland are described.

The role and impact of European Community legislation on UK contaminated land provision is addressed, and brief summaries presented on the legislative framework for contaminated land in the Netherlands, Germany, Denmark, the USA, Canada, Australia and New Zealand.

CONTENTS

1   **INTRODUCTION TO VOLUME XII**
    1.1   Introduction
    1.2   Legislation
    1.3   Purpose

Part A UK Contaminated Land Policy and Administration

2   **UK POLICY ON CONTAMINATED LAND**
    2.1   Introduction
    2.2   Current policy
    2.3   Development of policy
    2.4   Policy issues
    2.5   Other policy considerations
    References   12

3   **ADMINISTRATION OF POLICY AND LEGISLATION**
    3.1   Introduction
    3.2   National government departments
    3.3   National enforcement agencies
    3.4   Land reclamation agencies
    3.5   Local government departments
    References

Part B Legislation on Contaminated Land

4 INTRODUCTION TO LEGISLATION
- 4.1   Key legal requirements
- 4.2   Legislation in Scotland and Northern Ireland

5 PLANNING AND DEVELOPMENT CONTROL
- 5.1   Introduction
- 5.2   Land use policy
- 5.3   The definition of development
- 5.4   Planning powers with respect to development
- 5.5   Environmental assessment
- 5.6   Controls over building works
- References

6 OCCUPATIONAL HEALTH AND SAFETY
- 6.1   Introduction
- 6.2   Hazards arising at a place of work
- 6.3   Transporting and packaging hazardous materials
- 6.4   Other relevant legislation
- References

7 PUBLIC HEALTH
- 7.1   Introduction
- 7.2   Statutory nuisance
- 7.3   Occupiers' liability legislation
- References

8 ENVIRONMENTAL PROTECTION
- 8.1   Introduction
- 8.2   Environment Protection Act 1990 Part IIA - Contaminated Land
- 8.3   Air quality
- 8.4   Water quality
- 8.5   Waste management
- 8.6   Soil and land quality
- 8.7   Other environmental protection measures
- References

9 PROPERTY TRANSACTIONS AND LIABILITY
- 9.1   Introduction
- 9.2   Liability for contamination and its consequences
- 9.3   Parties to transactions
- 9.4   Caveat emptor
- 9.5   Contractual provisions
- 9.6   Provision in leases and mortgages
- 9.7   Property misdescriptions
- 9.8   Defective premises
- 9.9   Collateral warranties
- References

Part C European Community Environmental Policy

10 INTRODUCTION TO EUROPEAN POLICY AND LEGISLATION
- 10.1   Development of community environment policy
- 10.2   The institutions of the community

    10.3   Legislative instruments of the community
    10.4   Community environmental action programmes
    References

11 EUROPEAN COMMUNITY LEGISLATION AND INITIATIVES
      RELEVANT TO CONTAMINATED LAND
    11.1   Introduction
    11.2   Planning and development control
    11.3   Health and Safety
    11.4   Environmental protection
    11.5   Soil/land quality
    11.6   Liability and Environmental Damage
    References

Part D Contaminated Land Policy and Practice Overseas

12 CONTAMINATED LAND POLICY AND PRACTICE OVERSEAS
    12.1   Introduction
    12.2   Netherlands
    12.3   Germany
    12.4   Denmark
    12.5   Australia and New Zealand
    12.6   Canada
    12.7   The United States of America
    References

REFERENCES

ALLEN M, and MATHER, C. *Protecting the Community.* A London Hazards Centre Handbook. London Hazards Centre Trust Ltd (London), 1992

An act to amend the bankruptcy and insolvency act, the companies' creditors arrangement act and income tax act Bill C-5

ANON. *A rickety framework for contaminated land.* ENDS Report, No. 238, 1994, pp 15-19

ANON. *Britain and the EC move in step on groundwater protection.* ENDS Report, No. 202, November 1992

ANON. *Congress addresses need for redevelopment of industrial sites.* Hazardous Materials Control Resources Institute, FOCUS, 1993, 9(3), p6

ANON. *Environmental Themes for the UK Presidency.* ENDS Report, No. 210, July 1992

BORG, D. Status and future strategy concerning old waste disposal sites and industrial sites in Denmark. In: *Proceedings of the Second International TNO/BMFT Conference on Contaminated Soil.* Kluwer Academic Publishers (Dordrecht), 1988, pp 1537-1542

BRITISH DRILLING ASSOCIATION *Guidance notes for the safe drilling of landfills and contaminated land.* BDA (Brentwood), 1992

BUILDING RESEARCH ESTABLISHMENT. *Construction of new buildings on gas contaminated land.* BRE (Garston), 1991

BUILDING RESEARCH ESTABLISHMENT. *Radon: Guidance on protective measure for new dwellings.* BRE (Garston), 1991

BURNETT-HALL, R. Legal Aspects. In: *Proceedings of a Conference on Contaminated Land: Policy, Regulation and Technology.* IBC (London), 1990

CANADIAN COUNCIL OF MINISTERS OF THE ENVIRONMENT. *A framework for ecological risk assessment: general guidance.* PN 1195. CCME (Winnipeg), 1996

CANADIAN COUNCIL OF MINISTERS OF THE ENVIRONMENT. *Contaminated site liability report: recommendations and principles for a consistent approach across Canada.* CCME (Winnipeg), 1993

CANADIAN COUNCIL OF MINISTERS OF THE ENVIRONMENT *Environmental code of practice for above ground storage tank systems containing petroleum products.* PN 1144. CCME (Winnipeg), 1994

CANADIAN COUNCIL OF MINISTERS OF THE ENVIRONMENT. *Environmental code of practice for underground storage tank systems containing petroleum products and allied petroleum products.* PN1144. CCME (Winnipeg), 1994

CANADIAN COUNCIL OF MINISTERS OF THE ENVIRONMENT *Guidance manual for developing site specific soil quality remediation objectives for contaminated sites in Canada.* PN1197. CCME (Winnipeg), 1996

CANADIAN COUNCIL OF MINISTERS OF THE ENVIRONMENT. *Guidance manual as sampling, analysts and data management.* PN1103. CCME (Winnipeg), 1993

CANADIAN COUNCIL OF MINISTERS OF THE ENVIRONMENT. *Interim CCME Environmental Quality Criteria for Contaminated Sites.* Report CCME EPC-CS34. CCME (Winnipeg), 1991

CANADIAN COUNCIL OF MINISTERS OF THE ENVIRONMENT. *National classification system for contaminated sites.* Report CCME EPC-CS39F. CCME (Winnipeg), 1992

CANADIAN COUNCIL OF MINISTERS OF THE ENVIRONMENT. *Protocol for the derivation of environmental and human health soil quality guidelines.* PN1207. CCME (Winnipeg), 1994

CANADIAN COUNCIL OF MINISTERS OF THE ENVIRONMENT. *Subsurface assessment handbook for contaminated sites.* PN1144. CCME (Winnipeg), 1994

CANADIAN ENVIRONMENT COMPLIANCE MANUAL. CCH Canadian Ltd, 1997

CARTWRIGHT, B., MERRY, R.H., and TILLER, K.G. (1977) *Heavy Metal Contamination of Soils around a lead smelter at Port Pirie,* South Australia, *Australian Journal of Soil Research,* 11, pp.69-81 cited in Australia State of the Environment 1996, Department of the Environment, Sport and Territories, CSIRO Publishing, 1996, pp 6-33

CENTRE FOR EXPLOITATION OF SCIENCE AND TECHNOLOGY. *Contaminated land: market and technology issues.* CEST (London), 1992

CHURCH, T.W., NAKUMURA, R.T. and COOPER, P.J. *What works?: Alternative Strategies for Superfund Clean-ups.* Clean Sites Inc. (Alexandria VA), 1991

CIRIA. *Sale and transfer of land which may be affected by contamination.* Special Publication 99. CIRIA (London) [forthcoming]

CLEAN SITES. *Improving Remedy Selection: An Explicit and Interactive Process for the Superfund Program.* Clean Sites Inc. (Alexandria VA), 1990

CLR 6 – Prioritisation and categorisation procedure for sites which may be contaminated. Report by M J Carter Associates, DoE, 1995

Commission Decision of 20 December 1993 establishing a list of wastes pursuant to Article 1(a) of Council Directive 75/442/EEC on waste. *Official Journal*, NoL 5/15 (94/3/EC), January 1994

COMMISSION OF THE EUROPEAN COMMUNITIES (DIRECTORATE GENERAL XI). LIFE Information Pack, 1992

COMMISSION OF THE EUROPEAN COMMUNITIES: Green Paper on Remedying Environmental Damage. Communication from the Commission to the Council and Parliament and the Economic and Social Committee COM(93) 47, Final, May 1993

COMMISSION OF THE EUROPEAN COMMUNITIES. Fifth Action Programme for the Environment and Sustainable Development. *Official Journal*, C138/1, 17.5.93

CONFEDERATION OF BRITISH INDUSTRY. *Firm foundations.* CBI (London), 1993

COUNCIL OF EUROPE. *Convention on Civil Liability for Damage Resulting from Activities Dangerous to the Environment.* Available from HMSO Agency section

DEPARTMENT OF THE ENVIRONMENT. *A framework for assessing the impact of contaminated land on groundwater and surface water.* Contaminated Land Research Report. DoE (London), 1994

DEPARTMENT OF THE ENVIRONMENT. Ad-hoc International Working Group on Contaminated Land. Report on the Nottingham University, May 1994 meeting

DEPARTMENT OF THE ENVIRONMENT. *Arsenic-Bearing Wastes – A Technical Memorandum on Recovery, Treatment and Disposal including a Code of Practice,* Waste Management Paper No. 20. HMSO (London), 1980

DEPARTMENT OF THE ENVIRONMENT *Consultation on draft statutory guidance on contaminated land,* Vol I and II, September 1996

DEPARTMENT OF THE ENVIRONMENT. *Clinical Wastes – A Technical Memorandum on Arisings, Treatment and Disposal including a Code of Practice,* Waste Management Paper No. 25. HMSO (London), 1983

DEPARTMENT OF THE ENVIRONMENT. *Conclusions on the review of tree preservation orders.* DoE (London), 1994

DEPARTMENT OF THE ENVIRONMENT. *Development plans and regional planning guidance.* PPG Note 12. DoE (London), 1992, and PPG 12 (Wales), Development plans in Wales 1992

DEPARTMENT OF THE ENVIRONMENT. *Draft Environmental Protection Act 1990 (Section 143 Registers) Regulations.* Consultation Paper. DOE (London), 1992

DEPARTMENT OF THE ENVIRONMENT. *Environmental Protection Bill, Part 1 (Clause 2), Schedule of Prescribed Processes and Substances.* DoE (London), 1990

DEPARTMENT OF THE ENVIRONMENT. *ETIS: Government funding for environmental research projects.* DOE (London), 1992

DEPARTMENT OF THE ENVIRONMENT. *Guidance on the interpretation of major accidents to the environment for the purposes of the CIMAH Regulations.* DOE (London), 1991

DEPARTMENT OF THE ENVIRONMENT. *Halogenated Organic Wastes – A Technical Memorandum on Arisings, Treatment and Disposal including a Code of Practice.* Waste Management Paper No. 15. HMSO (London), 1980

DEPARTMENT OF THE ENVIRONMENT. *Heat-treatment Cyanide Wastes – A Technical Memorandum on Arisings, Treatment and Disposal including a Code of Practice.* Waste Management Paper No. 8. HMSO (London), 1976

DEPARTMENT OF THE ENVIRONMENT. *Landfill gas.* Waste Management Paper No. 27. HMSO (London), 1991

DEPARTMENT OF THE ENVIRONMENT. *Metal Finishing Wastes – A Technical Memorandum on Arisings, Treatment and Disposal including a Code of Practice,* Waste Management Paper No. 11. HMSO (London), 1976

DEPARTMENT OF THE ENVIRONMENT. *Mineral Oil Wastes – A Technical Memorandum on Arisings, Treatment and Disposal including a Code of Practice,* Waste Management Paper No. 7. HMSO (London), 1976

DEPARTMENT OF THE ENVIRONMENT. *Planning and the historic environment.* PPG Note 15. DoE (London), 1994

DEPARTMENT OF THE ENVIRONMENT. *Planning Controls over Sites of Special Scientific Interest.* Circular 1/92, 1992

DEPARTMENT OF THE ENVIRONMENT. *Polychlorinated Biphenyl (PCB) Wastes – A technical Memorandum of Reclamation, Treatment and Disposal including a Code of Practice.* Waste Management Paper No. 6. HMSO (London), 1976

DEPARTMENT OF THE ENVIRONMENT. *Review of radioactive waste management policy: Preliminary conclusions.* DoE (London), 1994

DEPARTMENT OF THE ENVIRONMENT. *Special Wastes. a technical memorandum providing guidance on their definition.* Waste Management Paper No. 23. HMSO (London), 1987

DEPARTMENT OF THE ENVIRONMENT. *Tarry and Distillation Wastes and Other Chemical Based Residues – A Technical Memorandum on Arisings, Treatment and*

DEPARTMENT OF THE ENVIRONMENT. *Planning Controls over Sites of Special Scientific Interest*. Circular 1/92, 1992

DEPARTMENT OF THE ENVIRONMENT. *Polychlorinated Biphenyl (PCB) Wastes – A technical Memorandum of Reclamation, Treatment and Disposal including a Code of Practice*. Waste Management Paper No. 6. HMSO (London), 1976

DEPARTMENT OF THE ENVIRONMENT. Profile of the English and Welsh Urban Development Corporations. Personal communication

DEPARTMENT OF THE ENVIRONMENT. *Review of radioactive waste management policy: Preliminary conclusions*. DoE (London), 1994

DEPARTMENT OF THE ENVIRONMENT. *Sampling strategies for contaminated land*. Contaminated Land Research Report. DoE (London), 1994

DEPARTMENT OF THE ENVIRONMENT. *Special Wastes: a technical memorandum providing guidance on their definition*. Waste Management Paper No. 23. HMSO (London), 1987

DEPARTMENT OF THE ENVIRONMENT. *Tarry and Distillation Wastes and Other Chemical Based Residues – A Technical Memorandum on Arisings, Treatment and Disposal including a Code of Practice*. Waste Management Paper No. 13. HMSO (London), 1977

DEPARTMENT OF THE ENVIRONMENT. *The Urban Regeneration Agency*. A Consultation Paper, 1992

DEPARTMENT OF THE ENVIRONMENT, SCOTTISH OFFICE ENVIRONMENT DEPARTMENT, WELSH OFFICE. *Surrender of Licences*. Waste Management Paper 26A (DOE/SOED/WO/1994)

DEPARTMENT OF THE ENVIRONMENT, SPORT AND TERRITORIES. *Australia State of the Environment 1996*. CSIRO Publishing, 1996, pp 6-33

DEPARTMENT OF THE ENVIRONMENT/WELSH OFFICE. *Planning and Compensation Act 1991: Implementation of the Main Enforcement Provisions*. Circular 21/91 (WO/91). HMSO (London), 1991

DEPARTMENT OF THE ENVIRONMENT/WELSH OFFICE *Environmental Assessment*. Circular 15/88 (WO/23/88). HMSO (London), 1988. And: *Permitted Development and Environmental Assessment*. Circular 3/95. HMSO (London), 1995

DEPARTMENT OF THE ENVIRONMENT/WELSH OFFICE. *Framework for Contaminated Land*. DoE (London), November 1994

DEPARTMENT OF THE ENVIRONMENT/WELSH OFFICE. *Planning Controls for Hazardous Substances. The Planning (Hazardous Substances) Act 1990. The Planning (Hazardous Substances) Regulations 1992 (SI 1992 No. 656)*. Circular 11/92 (20/92). HMSO (London), 1992

DEPARTMENT OF THE ENVIRONMENT/WELSH OFFICE. *Planning Controls over Demolition*. Circular 10/95 (WO 31/95). HMSO (London), 1995

DEPARTMENT OF THE ENVIRONMENT/WELSH OFFICE. *Development of contaminated land.* Circulars 21/87 and 22/87. DoE, WO (London, Cardiff), 1987

DEPARTMENT OF THE ENVIRONMENT/WELSH OFFICE. *Environmental Assessment: A guide to the procedures.* HMSO (London), 1989

DEPARTMENT OF THE ENVIRONMENT/WELSH OFFICE. *Paying for Our Past.* Consultation Paper. DoE/WO (London, Cardiff), March 1994

DEPARTMENT OF THE ENVIRONMENT/WELSH OFFICE. *Planning and Compensation Act 1991 - Planning Obligations,* Circular 16/91 (Welsh Office 53/91). HMSO (London), 1991

DEPARTMENT OF THE ENVIRONMENT/WELSH OFFICE. *Planning policy guidance on planning and pollution controls.* Planning Policy Guidance Note 23. HMSO (London), 1994 [replaces DoE Circular 21/87; in Wales the equivalent Circular WO212/87 still applies]

DEPARTMENT OF THE ENVIRONMENT/WELSH OFFICE. *Use of conditions in planning permissions.* Circular 11/95. HMSO (London), 1995

DEPARTMENT OF THE ENVIRONMENT/WELSH OFFICE/SCOTTISH OFFICE/NORTHERN IRELAND OFFICE. *Council Regulation No 259/93 on The Supervision and Control of Shipments of Waste within, into and out of the European Community, The Transfrontier Shipment of Waste Regulations 1994.* Circular 13/94 (DoE), 44/94 (WO), 21/94 (SOED), WM1/94 (DoE, NI)

DEPARTMENT OF THE ENVIRONMENT/WELSH OFFICE/SCOTTISH OFFICE. *Environmental Protection Act 1990, Waste Management, Duty of Care (COP).* HMSO (London), 1996

DEPARTMENT OF THE ENVIRONMENT/WELSH OFFICE/SCOTTISH OFFICE. *Environmental Protection Act 1990 Section 34, The Duty of Care.* Joint Circular 19/91 (Welsh Office 63/91, Scottish Office 25/91). HMSO (London), 1991

DEPARTMENT OF TRADE AND INDUSTRY. *DEMOS: DTI's Environmental Management Options Scheme.* DTI (London), 1991

DEPARTMENT OF TRADE AND INDUSTRY. *DTI's environmental schemes approved projects.* N13 BTF1.131. DTI (London), 1992

DZOMBAK, D.A., LABIENTEC, P.A. and SIEGRIST, R.L. The need for uniform soil clean-up values. *Environmental Science and Technology,* 1993, 27 (5), 765-766

EDULJEE, G. Application of risk assessment to contaminated land. In: *Proceedings of a Conference on Contaminated Land Policy, Economics and Technology.* Paper No. 2. IBC Technical Services (London), 1993

EEC Calls for tenders for contracts relating to waste management – 'Waste 92'. *Official Journal of the European Communities,* C87. Vol. 35, April 1992, p 11

ENVIRON CORPORATION. *Summary of major provisions of the New Jersey Department of Environmental Protection and Energy clean-up standards for contaminated sites, proposed new rules.* Environ Corporation (Princetown NJ), 1992

ENVIRONMENT AGENCY, Draft Management Statement, 6 December 1995

FEDERAL REMEDIATION TECHNOLOGIES ROUNDTABLE. *Synopses of Federal Demonstrations of Innovative Site Remediation Technologies.* EPA/540/8-91/009. US Environmental Protection Agency (Washington DC), 1991

FERGUSON, C. and DENNER, J. Soil remediation guidelines in the UK: A new risk-based approach. In: *Proceedings of a Conference on Developing Clean-up Standards for Contaminated Soil, Sediments and Groundwater.* Water Environment Federation (Alexandria VA), 1992, pp 205-211

GOVERNMENT OF THE UNITED KINGDOM OF GREAT BRITAIN AND NORTHERN IRELAND. Response to the Communication for the Commission of the European Communities (COM(93)47 Final) Green Paper on Remedying Environmental Damage. October 1993

GREEN, K.R. and EYRE, K. New Jersey's proposed new rules for clean-up standards for contaminated sites: a moving target. In: *Developing Clean-up Standards for Contaminated Soil, Sediment, and Groundwater: How Clean is Clean?* Water Environment Federation (Alexandria VA), 1993, p447-460

H M CUSTOMS AND EXCISE. *Reclamation of contaminated land,* Landfill Tax Information Note 1/97, 1 May 1997

HAIGH, N. *Manual of Environmental Policy: The EC and Britain.* Longman, (London), 1992

HALL, J.C. and HOWETT, C.M. Factors to consider in development of ARARs: is anyone doing it right? In: *Developing Clean-up Standards for Contaminated Soil, Sediment, and Groundwater: How Clean is Clean?* Water Environment Federation (Alexandria VA), 1993, p349-363

HARRIS, M.R. Recognition of the problem. In: *Reclaiming Contaminated Land.* Cairney, T.C. (ed.). Blackie (Glasgow), 1987, pp 1-29

HEALTH AND SAFETY EXECUTIVE. *Guide to Control of Industrial Accident Hazardous Regulations, 1984.* HS(R) 21 (REV). HMSO (London), 1990

HEALTH AND SAFETY EXECUTIVE. *Guide to the Reporting of Injuries, Diseases and Dangerous Occurrences Regulations 1985.* HMSO (London), 1995

HEALTH AND SAFETY EXECUTIVE *Management Health and Safety at Work and Construction (Design and Management Regulations) 1994.* HMSO (London), 1994

HEALTH AND SAFETY EXECUTIVE. *Notification and marking of sites.* The Dangerous Substances (Notification and Marking of Sites) Regulations 1990. HMSO (London), 1990

HEALTH AND SAFETY EXECUTIVE. *Occupational Exposure Limits.* EH40/96 HMSO (London), 1996

HEALTH AND SAFETY EXECUTIVE. *Protection of workers and the general public during development of contaminated land.* HS(G)66. HMSO (London), 1991

HER MAJESTY'S INSPECTORATE OF POLLUTION. *The Licensing of Waste Facilities.* Waste Management Paper No. 4. HMSO (London), 1994

HER MAJESTY'S INSPECTORATE OF POLLUTION. *Merchant and in house chemical waste incineration.* Chief Inspectors Guidance to Inspectors, Process guidance note IPR 5/1. HMSO (London), 1992

HODGE, S. Framework for land monitoring. *Industrial Waste Management,* September, 1993, pp 22-26

HOLTKAMP, A.B. and GRAVESTEYN, L.J.J. Large-scale voluntary clean-up operation for contaminated industrial sites in the Netherlands now on its way. In: *Proceedings of the Fourth International KfK/TNO Conference on Contaminated Soil.* Kluwer Academic Publishers (Dordrecht), 1993, pp 27-34

HOUSE OF COMMONS SELECT COMMITTEE ON THE ENVIRONMENT. *First report on contaminated land.* Three volumes. HMSO (London), 1990

Information systems for land contamination. Contaminated Land Research Report. DoE (London), 1994

JOHNSON, S.P. AND CORCELLE, G. *The Environmental Policy on the European Communities.* Graham and Trotman (London), 1990

MACRAE, J. Contamination list halted. *Estate Times,* 6 March, 1992

MATILLA, E.M. An EEC Commission Viewpoint. In: *Proceedings of a Conference on Contaminated Land Policy, Regulation and Technology.* Paper No. 4. IBC (London), 1990

MINISTRY OF AGRICULTURE, FISHERIES AND FOOD. *Good agricultural practice to protect soil.* MAFF (London), 1993

NATIONAL HEALTH AND MEDICAL RESEARCH COUNCIL OF AUSTRALIA/AUSTRALIA AND NEW ZEALAND ENVIRONMENT AND CONSERVATION COUNCIL. *Guidelines for the assessment and management of contaminated sites 1992*

NATIONAL RIVERS AUTHORITY. *Contaminated Land and the Water Environment.* Water Quality Series No. 15. HMSO (London), 1994

NATIONAL RIVERS AUTHORITY. *Policy and practice for the protection of groundwater.* National Rivers Authority (Bristol), 1992

NATIONAL RIVERS AUTHORITY. *Annual R&D Review – 1990.* National Rivers Authority. (Peterborough), 1991

NATO COMMITTEE ON CHALLENGES TO MODERN SOCIETY. *Final report of the demonstration of remedial action technologies for contaminated land and groundwater.* NATO/CCMS (Brussels), 1992

NATO COMMITTEE ON CHALLENGES TO MODERN SOCIETY. *Report of the NATO Committee on Challenges of Modern Society Pilot Study on Contaminated Land.* Plenum Press (New York), 1985

ONTARIO MINISTRY OF ENVIRONMENT AND ENERGY. *Guidance for use at contaminated sites in Ontario.* Publication Ontario (Toronto), 1997

ONTARIO MINISTRY OF ENVIRONMENT AND ENERGY. *Standard agreement concerning environmental Investigation.* 1996

PARLIAMENTARY OFFICE OF SCIENCE AND TECHNOLOGY. *Contaminated Land.* POST (London), 1993

Proposal for a Council Directive on Ambient Air Quality, Assessment and Management. *Official Journal,* 94/C 216/04, COM (94) 109 Final – 94/1106 (SYN)

Proposal for a Council Directive on the Control of Major Accident Hazards involving Dangerous Substances (COMAH). *Official Journal,* 94/C 106/04, COM (94) 4 Final – 93/0014 (SYN)

Proposal for a Council Directive on the Ecological Quality of Water. *Official Journal,* 94/C 222/06, COM (93) 680 Final

Proposal for a Council Directive on the Incineration of Hazardous Waste. *Official Journal,* 94/C 232/35

SARNO, D.J. Future use considerations in the clean-up of federal facilities. *Hazardous Materials Control, 1993 (May/June), 20-27 and 35*

SCOTTISH ENTERPRISE – Environmental Division (Land Engineering). Guidance note on project and programme rules. Scottish Enterprise (Glasgow), 1991

SCOTTISH OFFICE. *Contaminated land: Clean-up and control.* Consultation Paper. SO Environment Department (Edinburgh), March 1994

SIMMONS & SIMMONS. *Contamination, Remediation and Aggravation – A step by step guide to the new provisions contaminated land under the Environment Act 1995.* Simmons & Simmons (London)

STATE OF NEW JERSEY. *Technical basis and Background for Clean-up Standards for Contaminated Sites.* New Jersey Department of Environmental Protection, 1992

STATE OF NEW JERSEY. *Water Technical Programs, Ground Water Quality Standards, Proposed New Rules, NJAC 7:9-6.* New Jersey Register, 1992, 24, 18-201

STATE OF NEW JERSEY. Site Remediation Program, Cleanup Standards for Contaminated Sites, Proposed New Rules, NJAC:26D. *New Jersey Register,* 1992, 24, 373-403

STEEDS, J.A., SHEPHERD, E.L. and BARRY, D.L. *A guide to safe working practices for contaminated sites.* Report 132. CIRIA (London), 1996

STROBÆK, N. Contaminated sites in Denmark. In: *Proceedings of the Fifth International Conference of the NATO/CCMS Pilot Study on the Demonstration of Remedial Action Technologies for Contaminated Ground and Groundwater.* NATO/CCMS (Brussels), 1991

This Common Inheritance: Britain's Environmental Strategy, Cmd 1200. HMSO, (London), 1990

TROMANS, S. *The Environmental Protection Act 1990: Text and commentary.* Sweet and Maxwell (London), 1991

TURNER, R. *The role of planning authorities in influencing design of land treatment. In: Proceedings of an International Conference on Contaminated Land.* SCI Water and Environment Group (London), 1992

US ENVIRONMENTAL PROTECTION AGENCY. *An analysis of State Superfund Programs: 50-State Study, 1990 update.* EPA/540/8-91/002. USEPA Office of Emergency and Remedial Response (Washington DC), 1990

US ENVIRONMENTAL PROTECTION AGENCY. *Innovative Treatment Technologies: Semi-Annual Status report.* Fifth edition, EPA/542/R-93/003. USEPA Office of Solid Waste and Emergency Response (Washington DC), 1992

US ENVIRONMENTAL PROTECTION AGENCY. *The Superfund Innovative Technology EvaluationProgram: Annual Report to Congress 1992.* EPA/540/R-93/525. USEPA (Washington), 1993

US ENVIRONMENTAL PROTECTION AGENCY. *The Superfund Innovative Technology Evaluation Program: Technology Profiles.* Sixth edition, EPA/540/IR-93/526. USEPA Office of Solid Waste and Emergency Response (Washington DC), 1993

US ENVIRONMENTAL PROTECTION AGENCY REGION III. *Technical Guidance Manual: Risk Assessment: Selecting exposure routes and contaminants of concern by risk-based screening.* EPA/903/R-93-00. USEPA Region III (Philadelphia), 1993

Vessoso v Zanetti (1990) 2 LMELR, 133

WARREN SPRING LABORATORY. *Review of innovative contaminated soil clean-up processes.* LR 819 (MR). WSL (Stevenage), 1992

WELINDER, A.S. Property value and remediation: The Danish approach. In: *Proceedings of the Fourth International KfK/TNO Conference on Contaminated Soil.* Kluwer Academic Publishers (Dordrecht), 1993, pp 63-67

WELSH DEVELOPMENT AGENCY. *WDA Manual on the Remediation of Contaminated Land.* WDA (Cardiff), November 1993

WESTWOOD, T. Building control as a business. In: *Proceedings of the Annual Conference of the Incorporated Association of Architects and Surveyors, Scarborough, UK, 1991.* Paper No. 5, 1991

INDEX

Note: Numbers in italics refer to Tables. B indicates a Box, and Ap indicates an Appendix

air quality
  EC Directives *96*
    environmental control measures 161-2
    source control measures 161
  Scotland and Northern Ireland 98B
  UK legislation 93-5
  see also Clean Air Act (1993); Control of Pollution Act (COPA) (1974); Environmental Protection Act (EPA) (1990)
Air Quality Standards Regulations (1989) 95, 162
amenity, loss of and planning permission 41
ancient monuments 135
appropriate persons, cause of contamination 91
Approved Carriage List, for Proposed New Regulations on the Transport of Dangerous Goods 72
Approved Documents, status of 56
Approved Supply List, for dangerous substances 69, 70
aqueous environment, legislation for the protection of 101-3
assessment procedures 10
  DoE funded research 11B
  see also Environmental Protection Act (EPA) (1990)
Australia and New Zealand
  Australian National Health and Medical Research Council (NHMRC) 187
  Australian and New Zealand Environment and Conservation Council (ANZECC) 187
  Australian States arrangements 187, 188B
  emerging trends 190
  environmental problem, scale of 189
  funding remediation 189-90
  guidelines 187-9
  policy 186-7

Ballard v Tomlinson, nuisance, and an abstraction borehole 141-2
Basel Convention (1989) 130
best practicable environmental option (BPEO) 108

Borough Councils, powers of 5
Breach of Condition Notice, of planning permission 50-1
Building Act (1984) 57
Building (Approved Inspector) Regulations (1985) 28
building control function, local government 28
Building Regulations/building works
  and contamination 56-7
  general provisions 55-6
Building Research Establishment, funding 11

Cambridge Water Company vs Eastern Counties Leather plc case 6, 141
Canada
  Accord on Environmental Harmonisation 191
  British Columbia Contaminated Sites Regulation (CSR) 193-4, 196
  Contaminated Sites Advisory Group 191
  Environmental Appeal Board 196
  Federal site remediation liability policy 194-6
  leader and trustee liability 195-6
  lenders liability 195-6
  National Contaminated Sites Remediation Program (NCSRP) 191-2
  national policy 190-2
  Ontario's Environmental Protection Act (1990 and 1996) 192
  Ontario's remediation guidelines (1996) 193
  provincial policy 192-4
    liability 196
  Record of Site Clean-up (RSC) 193
  site-specific risk assessment (SSRA) 193
  Soil Quality Guidelines Task Group 192
Carriage of Dangerous Goods by Rail Regulations (CDG Rail2) 72
Carriage of Dangerous Goods by Rail Regulations (CDGR) (1994) *66*, 71
Carriage of Dangerous Goods by Road (Driver Training) Regulations (DTR2) 72

Carriage of Dangerous Goods by Road and Rail (Classification, Packaging and Labelling) Regulations (R&R(CLP)) (1994) *66*, 70, *71*

Carriage of Dangerous Goods by Road Regulations (CDG Road) 72

Carriage of dangerous Goods (Classification, Packaging and Labelling) and Use of Transportable Pressure Receptacles Regulations (CDGCPL2) 72

Carriage of Explosives by Road Regulations (CER2) 72

Carriage of Radioactive Materials by Rail (RAMRail) 72

caveat emptor, and contaminated land 146-7

change of use of land, and planning permission 43

Chemicals (Hazard Information and Packaging) Regulations (CHIP) (1993 and 1994), EC Directives *66*, 69-70, *71*, 159

Chemicals (Hazard Information and Packaging for Supply) Amendment Regulations (1996) *66*, 69-70, *71*
  European Economic Area Act (1993) 70

CIRIA, contaminated land research funding 11

Citizen's Charter 6

Clean Air Act (1993) 95

collateral warranties 149-50

common law, liability for leaching contaminants 141-5

Construction (Design and Management) Regulations (1994) 76-7, 77B

construction, new, consent for *45*

Consultation on Draft Statutory Guidance on Contaminated Land (DoE: 1996) 6

Contaminated Land: Clean-up and Control, Scottish consultation paper 4

Contaminated Land
  Environmental Agencies' responsibilities 18
  legislation relevant to *33*
  planning conditions with contamination 46-7
  remediation notices for 140
  see also Environmental Protection Act (EPA) (1990); liability for contamination

contamination
  and Building Regulations 56-7
  discussions with local authorities 46

liability for and its consequences 138-45
  as a material consideration 38
  Scotland and Northern Ireland 38B

contaminative uses register (EPA (1990) section 143) 38

contractual provisions, for sale and purchase agreements 147-8

Control of Industrial Major Accident Hazards Regulations (CIMAH) (1984) 74-5

Control of Pollution Act (COPA) (1974) 95, 105-6
  Amendment (1989) 128
  and waste management licensing 117, 118

Control of Substances Hazardous to Health (COSHH) (1994)
  assessment provision 64
  contaminants with separate provision 63
  duty on employers 63
  health surveillance provision 64
  information, instruction and training provision 64
  Maximum Exposure Limit (MEL) requirements 63
  monitoring employee exposure provision 64
  prevention or control of exposure provision 64
  Regulations (1988) 62
  use, maintenance, examination and test of control measures provision 64

controlled waste 115-16
  liability of occupiers of land with controlled wastes 139-40
  remedial powers for unlawfully deposited 129

Controlled Waste (Registration of Carriers and Seizure of Vehicles) Regulations (1991) 128

controlled waters *see* pollution of controlled waters; remediation of controlled waters

cost recovery, under Environmental Protection Act (EPA) (1990), Part IIA (1997?) – Contaminated Land 93

Dangerous Substances (Notification and Marking of Sites) Regulations (1990) 76

dangerous substances, transporting and packaging
  code of practice 69

duties of consignor 68B, 69
duties of driver 68B, 69
duties of vehicle operator 68B, 69
EC Hazardous Waste Directives 69,
    168-9
Hazardous Waste List 117
labelling requirements 70
legislation summary *66*
Proposed New Regulations on the
    Transport of Dangerous Goods 72
regulations for 65-72
Scotland and Northern Ireland 67B
see also waste; waste management
decommissioning, where consent
    required *45*
decontamination, where consent required
    45
Defective Premises Act (1972) 149
demolition
    and planning permission 41-2
    where consent required *45*
Denmark
    Chemical Waste Sites Act (1983) 186
    funding remediation 186
    Harbore Tange site 185
    National Environmental Protection
        Agency survey 185
    policy 185-6
    soil quality guidelines 186
Department of the Environment *see*
    Environment, Department of (DoE)
determinations, and planning permission
    43
development
    control of 44-5
    definition 39-45
    mechanisms for control 43
    planning powers for 46-51
development control system, for
    authorising development 43
development plans, statutory
    requirements of 37
    types of 36-7
dioxins and furans, EC Directives on
    emission of 161
Directive Waste 109-15
    and planning permission 43
discontinuance of use, and planning
    permission 42
District Councils, powers of 5
Duty of Care, EPA (1990) 20, *139*
Duty of Care Regulations (1991), for
    waste 127-8

effluents, legislation relating to discharge

99-100
emergency action, and planning
    permission 42
Employment Medical Advisory Service
    (EMAS) 21
Enforcement Notices, for breaches of
    planning control 50
    right of appeal 50
Enforcing Planning Control (PPG 18) 50
engineering operations, and planning
    permission 40
English Partnerships, purpose and
    function 27
Enterprise Zones 39
    and planning permission 44, 44B
Environment Act (1995) 3, 4, 86, 101
    see also Environmental Protection Act
        (EPA) (1990), Part IIA (1997?) –
        Contaminated Land
Environment Agency (EA)
    and the aqueous environment 101-3
    functions/responsibilities/objectives
        17-21, 17B
    and notices for removal of controlled
        waste 139-40
    pollution control duties 21
    powers of entry 129
    regulatory functions summary 20-1
    remediation of controlled waters,
        powers for 140-1
    role of 4-6, 15
    and Special Waste Regulations 117
    and water quality 97, 99-100
Environment, Department of (DoE)
    proposals and draft regulations (1990-
        93) 9
    responsibilities 15
Environment and Heritage Service,
    Northern Ireland,
    functions/responsibilities/objectives 18
Environmental Assessments
    need for 51-2
    for planning permission 45
    practical implications 54
    scope of 52-4, 53B
environmental health departments,
    involvement areas 28
Environmental Information Regulations
    (1992) 6
Environmental Management Option
    Scheme (DEMOS) (DTI), funding 11
Environmental Protection Act (EPA)
    (1990)
    ambient air quality 95-7
    and civil liability *139*, 144-5

contaminative uses register (section
143) 38
and control of discharges 98-9
and controlled waste 115-16
and EC Directives 161
emissions to atmosphere 97
local authorities duty to compile
information 9
Part IIA (1997?) – Contaminated Land
basis of new approach 86
guidance principle 86, 87B
main features 4-6
source-pathway-receptor approach
86
step 1 – local authority inspection
for contamination 87-8
step 2 – designation as a Special
Site? 88
step 3 – do other statutes apply? 88,
89B
step 4 – is urgent action needed? 89
step 5 – identification of responsible
people 89-90, 91B
step 6 – consultation on remediation
90
step 7 – restrictions on service
and/or remediation notice 91-2
step 8 – service of remediation
notice 92
step 9 – appeal against notice 92
step 10 – prosecution if necessary
92-3
step 11 – action by authority 93
step 12 – cost recovery 93
pollution control 18
and public health 79-81
specified contaminative uses 10B
and waste management 105-6
Environmental Protection (Prescribed
Processes and Substances) Regulations
(1991) 101B
Environmental Technology Innovation
Scheme (ETIS), funding 11
EUROENVIRON 11
European Community
environment policy 151-2
Environmental Action Programmes
purpose 151, 153
Fourth Programme 154
Fifth Programme 154-6
legislation on health and safety 158-60
Lugano Convention on Civil Liability
for Environmental Damage 177
planning and development control 157
European Community Commission 152

European Community Decisions 152-3
European Community Directives
air environmental quality 161-2
air quality source control 161
air quality standards *96*
authority of 152-3
Chemicals (Hazard Information and
Packaging) Regulations (CHIP)
(1993 and 1994) *66*, 69-70, *71*
disposal of sewage sludge to land 132
lead in air 162
nitrogen dioxide 162
soil/land quality 171
sulphur dioxide and suspended
particulates 161-2
thermal treatment plants 161
waste on contaminated land *166*
waste, existing provisions 166
waste framework Directive 167-8
waste, hazardous, Directive 117, 168-9
waste, incineration of hazardous 170-1
waste, on landfill, draft Directive 169-
70
water quality legislation *164*
water quality measures 165
water quality policy 162-3
water source control 163-5
European Community liability and
environmental damage Green Paper
action initiation 175
civil liability 173
compensation 175
damage definition 173-4
damage from waste 172
defences from liability 174-5
fault-based liability 173
insurance 175
retrospectivity 176
UK response to Green Paper 176
European Community Regulations 152-3
European Council of Ministers 152
European Court of Justice 152
European Parliament 152

Finance Act 1996 - Landfill Tax 131-2
Framework for Contaminated Land,
DoE/Welsh Office paper 4-5
funding for remediation 11-12
furans and dioxins, EC Directives on
emission of 161

General Development Orders (GDOs)
for authorising development 43
and planning permission 39, 40-1, 42
Germany

abandoned waste disposal sites 182
  funding remediation 185
  industrial sites 182
  policy 182-3
  registered and abandoned hazardous
    sites *184*
  Soil Protection Act 183
  three-stage remediation approach 183
  unification problems 183-5
Government departments 15-16
groundwater
  Policy and Practice for the Protection
    of Groundwater (NRA) 102-3
  quality/protection, EC Directives 163,
    164

hazardous materials *see* dangerous
  substances
Hazardous Waste List 117
health and safety, EC directives and UK
  implementation 158-60
Health and Safety at Work etc. Act
  (1974) 59-61
  other relevant legislation 72-7
  Regulations (1992) for management of
    61-3
  Regulations and Approved Codes of
    Practice *60*
  for Scotland and Northern Ireland 60B
  see also Control of Substances
    Hazardous to Health (COSHH)
    (1994); dangerous substances,
    transporting and packaging; Manual
    Handling Operations Regulations
    (1992); Personal Protective
    Equipment at Work Regulations
    (1992); Provision and Use of Work
    Equipment Regulations (1992);
    public health
Health and Safety Executive (HSE),
  function of 21, 59
Her Majesty's Inspectorate of Pollution
  (HMIP) 15
Highlands and Islands Enterprise (HIE)
  function and aims 24
House of Commons Select Committee on
  the Environment, (report 1990) 8

incineration of hazardous waste, EC
  Directive on 161
indemnities and warranties 147
Injunction Relief, application by local
  authority 51
innocent owners 90
Interdepartmental Committee for the

Redevelopment of Contaminated Land
  (ICRCL)
  membership 7B
  publications 7B

labelling requirements, dangerous
  substances 70
Land Drainage Act 98
Land Reclamation Agencies *see* English
  Partnerships; Scottish Enterprise (SE);
  Urban Development Corporations
  (UDCs); Welsh Development Agency
  (WDA)
Land Reclamation Programme Projects,
  funding 12
land use policy 36-9
land values, aesthetic, protection of 133
land/soil quality 132-4
Landfill Tax, Finance Act (1996) 131-2
landfill of waste, EC Directive 169-70
Latent Damage Act (1986) 145
lead in air, EC Directives on 162
leases, and contractual liability for
  contamination 148
legislation
  key issues for managing a
    contaminated site 34
  key requirements 31-2
  main legislation for contaminated land
    for England, Wales, Scotland and
    Northern Ireland *33*
  objectives, international 1-2
  in Scotland and Northern Ireland 32
lenders of money for land, liability for
  pollution 146
liability for contamination
  common law 141-5
  contaminated land remediation notices
    140
  controlled waste remediation 139-40
  controlled waters remediation 140-1
  sources of liability *139*
  water pollution offences 140
licensing *see* waste management
  licensing EPA section 33(1)
LIFE, financial support programme of the
  EC 155-6
Limitation Act (1980) 145
limitation period for legal action 145
local authorities
  and new provisions of the
    Environment Protection Act (1990)
    86-93
  power of, 1993 government review
    10B

public health responsibilities 80
Local Enterprise Companies (LECs)
  (Scotland) 16, 24-5, 24B
Local Government, Planning and Land
  Act (1980) 22
local government departments
  new contaminated land powers 28
  see also building control function;
    environmental health departments;
    Planning Authorities
London Waste Regulation Authority 20
Lugano Convention on Civil Liability for
  Environmental Damage 177

Maastricht treaty 155
Making Waste Work (DoE and Welsh
  Office) (1995) 108
Management of Health and Safety at
  Work Regulations (1992) 61-3, 62B
Manual Handling Operations Regulations
  (1992) 65
Manual on the Remediation of
  Contaminated Land (WDA) 26
Marine, Land and Liabilities Division of
  DoE, responsibilities 15
Maximum Exposure Limit (MEL),
  COSHH requirements 63
minerals local plan 36
Minerals Planning Authority 36
mortgages, and contractual liability for
  contamination 148

National Rivers Authority 19B, 47, 101-3
negligence, and the common law 144
Netherlands
  environmental policy 180-1
  funding remediation 181
  Interim Soil Clean-up Act 181
  multi-functionality principle 180, 182
  polluter pays principle 181
  Soil Protection Act (1987 and 1994)
    181
New Zealand *see* Australia and New
  Zealand
nitrogen dioxide, EC Directives on 162
Northern Ireland
  air quality legislation 98B
  Building Regulations and
    contamination 55B
  contamination as a material
    consideration 38B
  dangerous substances, transporting and
    packaging 67B
  development, definition of 39B
  Environmental Assessments 54B

Health and Safety Agency 21
Health and Safety at Work 60B, 73B
  legislation relevant to contaminated
    land *33*
  Occupiers' Liability (Northern Ireland)
    Orders (1957 and 1987) 84B
  planning obligations 48B
  provisions for planning permission
    46B
  Statutory Nuisance 82B
  waste management 110B
  water quality legislation 104B
Northern Ireland Office (NIO),
  responsibilities 16, 16B
Notification of Installations Handling
  Hazardous Substances (NIHHS)
  Regulations (1982) 75
nuisance, and the common law 141-3,
  144

occupiers of land, liability for pollution
  145-6
Occupiers' Liability Act (1957 and 1984)
  83-4
  Scotland and Northern Ireland 84B
orphan groundwaters 90
orphanage liabilities 5
owners of land, liability for pollution
  145-6
ozone air pollution, EC Directives on 162

packaging dangerous/hazardous materials
  see dangerous substances, transporting
    and packaging
Paying for Our Past, consultation paper
  3-4
permission *see* planning permission
Personal Protective Equipment at Work
  Regulations (1992) 65
Planning Agreements 47-8, 49
Planning Authorities, local government
  27-8
Planning and Compensation Act (1991)
  36, 37, 42, 47
Planning Contravention Notice, for
  planning control 51
planning and development control, EC
  Directive on 157
Planning (Hazardous Substances)
  Regulations (1992) 76
planning obligations 47-51
planning permission
  assessing need for 40-3
  and change of use 43
  development, definition of 43

enforcement 49-51
and Enterprise Zones 44, 44B
provisions for Scotland and Northern
Ireland 46B
and Simplified Planning Zones 44
when needed 39-40
where there is contamination 46-7
see also Environmental Assessments
Planning Policy Guidance (Note 23) 38
Policy and Practice for the Protection of
Groundwater (NRA) 102-3
policy, UK
current 3-6
development of 6-8
issues 8-12
polluter pays policy 4, 5
pollution control, Environmental
Agencies' responsibilities 18
pollution of controlled waters
from discharges 99-100
landowners responsibilities 140
Water Resources Act (1991) *139*, 140
private nuisance 144
Property Misdescriptions Act ((1991)
148-9
protected species 134
Provision and Use of Work Equipment
Regulations (1992) 64-5
public health
occupiers liability legislation 83-4
Scotland and Northern Ireland 82B,
84B
statutory nuisance 79-82
public nuisance 144

Radioactive Substances Act (1993) 131
radioactive waste 117
Registration of waste brokers 128-9
remedial operations, consent for *45*
remedial works, and planning permission
41
remediation of controlled waters 140-1
remediation notices/statements 90, 91-3,
139, 140
Reporting of Injuries, Disease and
Dangerous Occurrences Regulations
(RIDDOR) (1995) 75
risk assessment procedures, DoE funded
research 11B
River Purification Authority (Scotland)
47
Road Traffic (Carriage of Dangerous
Substances in Packages etc.)
Regulations (PGR) (1992) *66*, 67-8,
68B

Road Traffic (Carriage of Dangerous
Substances in Road Tankers and Tank
Containers) Regulations (RTR) (1992)
66, 68-9
Royal Commission on Environmental
Pollution (1996) 133
Rylands v Fletcher and the contaminated
bore hole 141-3, 144

Scotland
air quality legislation 98B
Building Standards Regulations and
contamination 55B
civil remedies in 142B
Contaminated land: Clean-up and
control, consultation paper 4
contamination as a material
consideration 38B
dangerous substances, transporting and
packaging 67B
development, definition of 39B
Environmental Assessments 54B
Health and Safety at Work 60B, 73B
Her Majesty's Industrial Pollution
Inspectorate (HMIPI) 15
legislation relevant to contaminated
land *33*
Local Enterprise Companies (LECs)
16, 24-5, 24B
Occupiers' Liability (Scotland) Act
(1960) 84B
planning obligations 48B
provisions for planning permission
46B
River Purification Authority 47
Statutory Nuisance 82B
waste management 110B
water quality legislation 104B
Scottish Enterprise and Highlands and
Islands Enterprise 16
Scottish Enterprise (SE), function and
aims 24
Scottish Environment Protection Agency
(SEPA)
functions/responsibilities/objectives 17,
18
pollution control duties 21
Scottish Office Environmental
Department 16
Scottish Office Industry Department 16
Scottish Office (SO) 19
sewerage systems, discharges to 100
Simplified Planning Zones 39
and planning permission 44
site investigation

consent for *45*
  for planning permission 40-1
site notices, for planning 42
Sites of Special Scientific Interest (SSSIs)
  134
soil/land quality 132-4
  EC Directives 171
  EC policy 154
special waste 116
Special Waste regulations (1996) 116,
  117
statutory duty, common law for breach of
  144
Statutory Water Companies Act 98
Stop Notice, for breaches of planning
  control 50
sulphur dioxide and suspended
  particulates, EC Directives on 161-2
Supplementary Credit Approvals (SCA)
  system 15
sustainable development
  as an EC policy 154
  as a UK policy 4
Sustainable Development – the UK
  strategy (1994) 108-9
Sustainable Use of Soil, Royal
  Commission on Environmental
  Pollution (1996) 133

test of reasonableness 49
thermal treatment plants, EC Directives
  on 161
Town and Country Planning Act (1990)
  37, 43, 47, 48, 50
Town and Country Planning (Demolition
  – Description of Buildings) (1992) 42
Town and Country Planning General
  Development Order (1992) 42
transporting dangerous/hazardous
  materials *see* dangerous substances,
  transporting and packaging
Tree Preservation Orders 134-5
Trespass, and the common law 144

UK Transfrontier Shipment of Waste
  Regulations (1994) 130
Unitary Development Plan 36, *37*
United States of America
  Applicable or Relevant and
    Appropriate Requirements (ARARs)
    199B
  Brownfields initiatives 199
  California Environmental Quality Act
    (CEQA) 202
  Clean Sites Inc 201-2, 202B

Comprehensive Response,
  Compensation and Liability Act
  (CERCLA) (1980) 197-8, 199, 199B
Environmental Cleanup Responsibility
  Act 202
Federal programmes 197-202
Federally-owned lands programmes
  200
Membership of Federal Remediation
  Technology Roundtable 201B
National Contingency Plan and the
  National Priorities List 198B, 201
policy 197
'polluter pays' policy 197
Radio Studies Division (RSD) of the
  Office of Radiation Programs (ORP)
  199-200
Resource Conservation and Recovery
  Act (1976) 197B
State and local programmes 202-3
Superfund Innovative Technology
  Evaluation Program 200B
Superfund legislation 197-9, 198B,
  202
Technology Innovation Office 201B
Urban Development Corporations
  (UDCs)
  powers 22
  profile of English and Welsh *23*
Use Class Order, for authorising
  development 43

warranties and indemnities 147
  collateral warranties 149-50
Warren Spring Laboratory, funding 11
waste
  controlled waste 115-16
    remedial powers for unlawfully
      deposited 129
  directive waste, definition 109-15, *111*
  discarded waste 113-14
  and Duty of Care Regulations (1991)
    127-8
  flytipping 128
  hazardous waste 116
  industrial waste 116
  international colour coding 130
  'keeping' and EPA (section 33) 120
  special waste 116
    see also Special Waste Regulations
  substances not Directive Waste 113
  substances/objects that are waste when
    discarded 112B
  toxic waste 116
  see also dangerous substances,

transporting and packaging
waste brokers, registration 128-9
Waste Framework Directive 113
waste local plan 36
waste management
  chain of utility 114-15
  commercial cycle for 114-15
  controls over international movement 130
  disposal/recovery operations and EPA (section 33) 118
  DoE published papers 108B
  EC Directives
    existing provision 166
    Framework Directive 167-8
    Hazardous Waste Directive 168-9
    incineration of hazardous 170-1
    landfill of waste 169-70
    obligations on member states 167-8
    Waste Management Plans 168
  key licensing documents 106B
  legislation based on Control of Pollution Act (1974) 105-6
  national strategy 108-9
  normal commercial cycle 114
  planning permission for deposit of 43
  Scotland and Northern Ireland 110B
  specialised recovery operations 114-15
  UK policy 107
  waste generated at a contaminated site *105*
waste management licensing EPA section 33(1)
  and COPA waste licensing provisions 117, 118, 125
  defences and penalties 123-4
  deposit/disposal of waste 118
  EPA Part II 117
  excluded activities 122B
  fit and proper persons 124
  granting of licenses 124-5
  guidance on licence conditions 124
  'keeping' waste 120
  knowingly causing a deposit 120
  licence surrender 126-7
  licensing exemptions 122, 123B
  licensing requirements *119*
  mobile plants 120-1
  and planning permission 125
  revocations 126

  supervision 127
  suspensions 126
  unlawful deposits 120
  variations 125
  Waste Management Licensing Regulations (1994) 109, 125
waste regulation, Environmental Agencies' responsibilities 19-20
Waste Regulation Authorities 117
  powers of entry 129
Water Act (1989) 97-9
Water Consolidation Consequential Provisions Act (1991) 98
Water Industry Act (1991) 98
water pollution *see* pollution of controlled waters
water quality/protection
  abstraction of water 103-5
  acts since Water Act (1989) 97-9
  discharge to controlled waters 99-100
  discharge to sewerage systems 100
  EC Directives
    contaminated sites 163
    current legislation *164*
    dangerous substances 164
    grey list 165
    groundwater 163, 164
    inland/coastal/territorial waters 163
    policy for 162-3
    quality measures 165
    source control 163-5
  EC policy 155
  Environmental Agencies' responsibilities 19
  Environmental Protection Act (1990) 98-9
  protection of the aqueous environment 101-3
  Scotland and Northern Ireland 104B
  Water Industry Act (1991) 98
Water Resources Act (1991) 90, 98, 99-100, *99*, 101, 103-5, *139*, 145
Welsh Development Agency (WDA)
  aims/functions/activities/structure 25-6, 26B
  land reclamation data 26B
  research programme 16
Welsh Office (WO), policy input 16
Wildlife and Countryside Act (1981) 134

FURTHER READING

Other CIRIA titles covering contaminated land issues include the following:

<u>Reports</u>
R130   Methane: its occurrence and hazards in construction
R131   The measurement of methane and other gases from the ground
R132   A guide for safe working on contaminated sites
R149   Protecting development from methane
R150   Methane investigation strategies
R151   Interpreting measurement of gas in the ground
R152   Risk assessment for methane and other gases from the ground

<u>Special Publications</u>
SP79   Methane and associated hazards to construction: a bibliography
SP99   Guidance on the sale and transfer of land which may be affected by contamination [forthcoming]
SP119   A guide for safe working on contaminated sites – poster set
SP124   Barriers, liners and cover systems for containment and control of land contamination
SP143   Assessment and treatment of contaminated land – speaker's notes

<u>Project Reports</u>
PR5   Methane and associated hazards to construction – research and information needs
PR34   Framework protocol for reporting the demonstration of land remediation technologies
PR35   Rapid characterisation of contaminated land using electrical imaging
PR36   In-situ remediation of soil and ground water contaminated with toluene

<u>Construction Industry Environmental Forum speakers' notes</u>
CIEFN23   Contaminated land: technologies and implementation
CIEFN24   Contaminated land: insurance and liabilities in sale and transfer
CIEFN59   Contaminated land
Forthcoming   Environmental risk assessment for contaminated land. New developments (Manchester, 17 February 1998)

<u>Funders Report</u>
FR/CP/26   Hydraulic control and pump-and treat systems